10-20-12

Creating Connection

Be curious.
Discover your story with new eyes.

Rebecca Thompson

Creating Connection:

Essential Tools for Growing Families through Conception, Birth and Beyond

By Rebecca Thompson, M.S.

The Consciously Parenting Project, LLC

Most of the personal stories in this book are either composite portraits or identifying characteristics have been changed or eliminated in order to protect the privacy of individuals.

The views expressed in this book are the author's own. If you have any concerns about any aspect of your child's behavior, health, or well-being, it is recommended that you seek professional advice. Neither the author nor the publisher shall be liable or responsible for any loss or damage allegedly arising from any information or suggestions in this book.

Published in the United States by
The Consciously Parenting Project, LLC

Paperback Version
Original Source: Creating Connection: Essential Tools for
Growing Families through Conception, Birth and Beyond
October 2012 edition
ISBN: 978-0-9842756-6-3

Original Process: The Consciously Parenting Project, LLC
Created by: The Consciously Parenting Project, LLC

Illustrations by: Susan Graham
Conversion Services by: Lianne March
Book Design by: Lianne March

Special thanks to Shannon Livingston of Livingston Galleries
for the cover photo. http://www.shannonlivingston.com

View My Website:
http://www.consciouslyparenting.com
http://www.holisticfamilyconsultant.com
E-mail me: rebecca@consciouslyparenting.com

For Ryan, Zack, and Josh, with gratitude for your love, your support, and for sharing the journey. And for Jacob.

Without you and all you've taught me, this book would not have been possible.

With appreciation:

I am so very grateful for all the support I've had over the years it has taken me to write this book from many, many people. Without all the encouragement, support while scribbling on napkins, and listening to me talk endlessly about these ideas, this would simply not have been possible. I would need to write another book to thank everyone adequately, but I'll do my best in the space I have.

Special thanks to Lianne March, without whom The Consciously Parenting Project and this book would not have been possible. Thank you for seeing the vision and helping me to make all this a reality, for late night e-mails and brainstorms. You have my heartfelt thanks.

Amy Rost, the best book midwife ever. Thank you for your time, your attention, your passion, and going above and beyond the call of duty to help breathe life and clarity into this book.

With appreciation to Bethany Shetler, Wilma Vance, Sally Flintoff, MaryJo McHaney, Ammana Shaka, and Valerie Groves for your encouragement, your wisdom, and your passion for families who have adopted or fostered children. Your contributions to the earliest versions of this book were essential to its development.

To my friends who supported and encouraged me through the ups and downs of writing and life: Susan Graham, my cruising buddy, for your saint-like support and willingness to listen and wait, and to draw on napkins and other table coverings with me. Debra Hart for living life on the other side of the worm hole, for reminding me to sing, for your honesty and clarity. Lu Hanessian for helping me remember why I'm doing this, for seeing what others couldn't see, for belly laughs and pillow fights. Janet Conner for providing so much more than a space to write.

For professional inspiration that has deeply affected my work, thank you to Pam Leo, Ray Castellino, Mary Jackson, Lu Hanessian, Suzanne Arms, and Carrie Contey. Thank you for lighting the way for so many families around the world.

Special thanks to my book readers. I appreciate your feedback to help make this book user-friendly: Erika S., Evelyn K., Lisa, Debra and Riley, David and Fran, Lianne, Ellen O., Becca, Janet, Lisa W., Tiffany C., Theresa, Sally, Bethany, MaryJo, Wilma.

I am eternally grateful to all the families I've worked with over the years who have taught me so much about life, love, and the importance of remaining open and curious about ourselves and our loved ones. It isn't always the journey we thought we were going on, but it is the journey we were meant to make.

Rebecca Thompson, MS, MFT
Crystal Beach, FL
October, 2012

Contents

Introduction

About Consciously Parenting

Consciously Parenting is part of a growing movement of parents around the world who are embracing the importance of relationship as a guiding compass, rather than focusing on behaviors as simply an inconvenience. Consciously Parenting is based on current research from divergent fields, helping us to find a way back to our own inner guidance. The research really supports deep connection with our children. When we have lost our way as a parent (and we all have at one point or another), Consciously Parenting is about bringing us back to our own inner knowing and finding connection with our kids and with our family again or for the first time.

In Book I, *Consciously Parenting*, we explored the 8 guiding principles of Consciously Parenting. While most parenting "experts" focus on getting behaviors to stop, research shows that the most important part of parenting is the relationship. Focusing on the relationship and seeking to understand the communication behind the behaviors leads us back into connection. At its heart, *Consciously Parenting* is about connecting with our own inner guidance system. When we can find our own inner voice, it is much more valuable than any so-called outside parenting "expert". Book I gives readers a map and compass for navigating the shift from a focus on behaviors to a focus on relationships in their families.

Book II, *Creating Connection*, focuses on the early patterns of relationships and how behaviors communicate more of our own unique story. When we understand the story, we can shift the relationship patterns in new and innovative ways. See "About this book" below for more information about this particular book.

Book III, *Nurturing Connection*, explores the importance of emotional connection in our relationships. When we're having a rough day or something happens and our child is upset, we often feel like we've done something wrong. If we're not happy or our child isn't happy (or can't be easily soothed), we think we're not succeeding as a parent. *Nurturing Connection* reminds us all that those moments of dysregulation, of "yellow light" moments for parents and children, can be some of the most connecting of all. We just need to realize that and embrace those moments. *Nurturing Connection* gives parents practical suggestions taken from real life situations that can be immediately applied in your family. (Watch for Book III in March 2013)

Book IV, *Healing Connection*, is the heart and soul of Consciously Parenting. Life happens. We say things we don't mean. We yell. We repeat things our parents said to us that we said we'd never say to our children. The marriage ends. Someone gets really sick. Grandma passes away. This is life. So how do we connect with our loved ones and repair connection in times like these? Are there times when relationships can't be repaired? What does repair look like after adoption? How can we repair a connection with our child after a rough start? *Healing Connection* explores this very important topic, essential for all families who want to create healthy relationships. Attachment and connection both require a working knowledge and application of repair. *Healing Connection* gives you the tools and understanding to move into more peace and harmony, regardless of life's circumstances. (Watch for Book IV in October 2013)

About This Book

The story of your family begins long before the conception of your first child and even long before your own conception. Patterns in families, for better or worse, don't just show up out of the blue. Instead, patterns emerge as living and breathing parts of our lives through the stories we tell to ourselves and to our children, spoken or unspoken. Even though we cannot consciously remember our early lives, the memories live on in our bodies, in cellular memory. The imprint of how we were conceived, whether we were expected or wanted, how our parents adjusted to the news, and how we came into the world, are all part of our stories. And they are part of our children's stories. What is not "remembered" consciously has a strong influence over our relationships, for better or for worse.

When we can understand our own story or the story of our child, we can make more sense of our struggles. For parents who have never connected deeply with one child, a closer look at the child's early story can often shed light on why. A child with behavioral challenges can be understood in a different light when we revisit the whole story, rather than trying to figure out how to just make the behaviors stop. When we understand the bigger story and how that interacts with our own story, we can start to make lasting changes in our families.

Creating Connection gives you the tools and information necessary to support your growing family, whether you are beginning the journey of parenthood prior to conception, are expecting your first baby, or are a veteran parent. The information in this book will support you on your own journey of self-understanding, as well as understanding your child more deeply.

Even if you didn't have a great beginning yourself or there were significant challenges in your child's early life, know that there is always hope. Families are resilient. It isn't about having the perfect set of events, but in understanding your family's story and using some of the tools suggested to reconnect or repair those early bumps in your journey. Remember that now!

Creating Connection isn't about creating another reason to beat yourself up because this or that happened or didn't happen. *Creating Connection* opens the doors to deeper understanding so you can create more connection in your family starting today.

Chapter One

The Importance of Creating Healthy Relationships

Although the impact of parental influence on children has been the source of much debate and the subject of many books in recent years, we now know that parents' influence on their children far outweighs the influences of genetics and even children's temperaments. This is good and bad news. It means that we aren't destined to have bad relationships with our children because it was "in the genes"; instead, we have the opportunity to establish or change the course of our relationships with them.

While our children have a part in the relationships, the younger the children are (chronologically or emotionally), the more the relationships are our responsibility. Young children need our loving guidance. They need us to create a structure that enables them to learn more about themselves and their own needs until they are aware of their own needs and can communicate those needs for themselves. And they need us to be there for them, guiding their journey much longer than perhaps we'd like to think.

As parents, we need facts, awareness, and support to create healthy relationships with our children. Much of the parenting information our own parents had was based on assumptions about children that have since been proven false, yet our own parenting decisions are likely to be based upon the decisions our parents made, for better or for worse. Remember that the attachment patterns we had with our parents early in our lives create the patterns for all of our future relationships, including, most profoundly, those with our own children. While some people know that they don't want to repeat the same patterns from their own childhood, they may find themselves still making the same decisions or sounding just like their own parents.

If we aren't aware of new parenting information and aware of the ways our parents' parenting decisions still affect us on a subconscious level, we will find ourselves parenting from an unconscious place. Parenting from this place could work well if your parents were conscious themselves, but not so well if they weren't. The patterns established during our own early care run deep. Our attachment status during our first three years of life dramatically influences our decisions and our ability to make the best decisions possible for our own very young children, yet it is unlikely we have any conscious memories of our early care.

Fortunately, parenting is healing work. It provides opportunities for us to see ourselves and our own stuck points through the eyes of our children in a way that no other situation can. And when we do our own healing work, we are much more able to be healthy parents.

As we explore the idea of creating relationships, we'll take a look at what is understood about brain development in young children and what that understanding means for our parenting decisions. We'll look at strategies for meeting our children's early needs and, in doing so, getting our relationships with them off to the best start possible. We'll take a look at stress and trauma in early development, because understanding these factors can guide our decision-making process and help us wade through the sea of parenting (mis)information flooding our culture.

This book may evoke strong feelings about your own unmet needs. If these feelings come up, simply observe them, then seek the support of friends or family members who can listen to you and hear what you have to say. If you are over-whelmed, please seek the assistance of a professional. (See the resources section for suggestions.) If you have already been through some of these stages with your children, and you realize there may have been an impact from events or circumstances that already happened, know that current brain science gives us much hope for repairing those relationships no matter how old your children are now. Book IV: *Healing Connection* (October 2013), goes into great detail about how reconnection and healing happen in families.

What Is a Healthy Relationship?

Now, before we continue, is a wonderful time to pause and address this question. The answers will help create a foundation for your early parenting decisions, since most of us have had few healthy relationships on which to base our decisions. After many discussions with clients and people in my classes, my colleagues and I have come up with the following definition: *A healthy relationship is one in which each person is aware of his or her own feelings and needs while being respectful of others' feelings and needs.* It also includes the ability to set boundaries by understanding what our responsibilities are with regard to our feelings and needs, and the ability to use that understanding in our relationships as our children grow.

We are responsible for meeting our young children's physical and emotional needs until they can do so for themselves. Paying attention to what we feel, especially when we are with our young children, can sometimes give us a clue as to what our children may be feeling, because we are so intimately connected with them in relationship. For years—not months—it is our job to mirror what our children feel and need so that they can learn to identify what they are feeling and needing, keeping in mind guiding principle 3, which reminds us that "a need, when met, will go away." We often automatically mirror what our children are experiencing. For example, when your baby smiles at you, you probably can't help but smile back.

Yet we need to be aware of our own feelings and needs and differentiate the feelings and needs that belong to us from those that belong to our children. While we are responsible for meeting our young children's needs, at the same time, we are also responsible for meeting our own. Some parents neglect and negate their own needs in their well-meaning attempts to meet their baby's every need; however, a relationship where one person's needs and feelings are deemed not important cannot be a healthy relationship.

The greater our own self-awareness, the easier it is to see what feelings belong to us and what feelings belong to our children. When we can recognize what belongs to us and what belongs to someone else, we are in a much better place to have a peaceful, happy family.

As our children grow, they can take more responsibility for identifying and meeting their needs in the moment while we watch closely. Our children fluctuate, just like we adults do, from day to day and moment to moment. Sometimes they are able to do more than at other times. Sometimes our children need our help to regulate their bodies, their emotions, and their behavior; other times, they can regulate themselves. We need to remember that our children are always doing the best they can do, just like we are. We also need to allow our children to learn and develop on their own timetable—not ours or that of a book we've just read.

A Note on Emotional Age

In our culture, we are very focused on how we think individuals of a certain age should act. While I believe it is important to have some benchmarks to let us know when something in our children's development is amiss, I also believe we often miss the meaning behind children (or adults) acting much younger than their chronological age.

Most of us have encountered adults who seem like three-year-olds when something isn't going their way, or ten-year-olds who throw toddler-like temper tantrums. This emotional-age discrepancy happens when there is an unresolved issue or an unmet developmental need, many times resulting from a past trauma the person may or may not remember. Regressions can occur in a nanosecond and can make

(continued)

someone appear much younger than they are chronologically. Children (and adults) with significant trauma
histories, especially, can act much younger than their
chronological age when they are stressed out.

If your child is consistently acting younger than
his chronological age, look at the age range that coin-
cides with how he is acting rather than how old he is
chronologically. Then respond to him as if he actually
were that regressed age. For example, if your ten-year-
old throws a tantrum like a three-year-old, respond as
if you were helping a three-year-old regulate his emotions. Respond, without judgment, to how the child is
acting in the moment—not how you think he should be
acting. Responding in this way actually allows the child
to return to his chronological age and learn the pattern
of regulation through repetition, thereby changing his
nervous system; eventually, the new patterns will enable him to regulate himself.

Shifting our expectations of our children, realizing that they are doing the best they can in the moment, allows space for healing to happen and for our
relationship to blossom.

The Beginning of Relationships

Relationships begin before children are born and more likely
even before conception, as indicated by the emerging fields of
epigenetics and pre- and perinatal psychology. Our children
are not born as blank slates, but absorb what happens to them
prenatally, during birth, and in the period of infancy they can't
consciously remember. Our early parenting decisions help form
the basic structure of a child's brain in the early years, while later

decisions only add to or lessen the impact of the basic structure. If Sarah feels loved and valued as an infant, for example, then later, when she is older and other people express love and Sarah's value, those expressions will resonate within her, because love and accepting love are part of her basic beliefs. On the other hand, if Sarah does not have this early experience, she will discount casual comments about her value or lovability because she does not hold these core beliefs about herself. Loving and valuing our babies, through meeting the needs discussed in this chapter, establishes strong neural pathways in their brains that enable them to believe they are loved and valued.

Because early parenting decisions make such an impact on children's development and the course of the parent-child relationship, it is vital that parents try to meet children's needs when they are young. It is possible to change things later, but because you are looking at changing the structure of the brain and the neural pathways, it requires *lots* of work on a daily basis.

We should do everything we can to prepare to create healthy relationships with our children *and* forgive ourselves for not being able to be perfectly prepared. We may not do *everything* right, but we can do *enough* right to establish a solid foundation. When I started my parenting journey, I was wide awake and intent on understanding and meeting the needs of my baby. I read every book that I could find about attachment needs and what they meant, to meet the physical and emotional needs of my baby. I looked carefully at my parenting decisions and sought the advice and wisdom of my midwife, Debbie Marin of the Hollywood Birth Center in Hollywood, Florida. I didn't always like what she said, and sometimes the books she suggested challenged me in ways I did not expect. Sometimes I almost dreaded what she was going to tell me to think about or what book she was going to tell me to read. My goodness, how many decisions were there to make before the baby had even arrived?

Even with all that preparation, I still managed to miss some important pieces of the puzzle regarding what my baby needed. Had I read about the importance of a tranquil womb environment and how important it was for moms to decrease their stress during pregnancy, I probably wouldn't have worked more than seventy hours a week with troubled families, doing home visits and working in two different clinics in two different counties in urban South Florida.

I didn't do everything perfectly, but I was distinctly aware of my choices, even if I didn't always like them and sometimes wished I didn't have all the information I had. Looking back now, I am grateful for all the information, and I know that my decisions were as informed as I could handle at the time. I have no regrets. I encourage you to adopt a similar mentality as you read the information in this book, frequently releasing any guilt that may come up if your past decisions differ from what you might choose today if you had it to do over. Start now, where you are, with your new information, and continue through the books in the Consciously Parenting series with me as I expand on ways to help heal experiences from the past that need to be healed.

Parental Consciousness

Being conscious and aware of ourselves is critical when we are parenting young children. Children do have biological expectations about the things they need to grow optimally; they are hardwired for lots of physical touch, for example, but they don't enter the world with preconceived ideas about the way things are supposed to be. Instead, they look to their parents to teach them about the world. Children do not enter the world with the same level of consciousness that adults have, yet adults interpret children's behaviors as if they do. Infants and young children are accused of higher level thinking, such as manipulation, when we know from studies of the brain that they are incapable of such thinking. When our thoughts, words, feelings, and actions suggest that a child is manipulating us, they will learn to manipulate because that's what we expect of them.

At the same time that we expect so much from our young children, we are also not aware of how sentient our babies actually are prenatally, as well as during and immediately after birth. We don't always treat our babies as if they are aware beings who are soaking up everything that is happening to them. Awareness is the first step in parental consciousness.

Good-enough parenting relies on our ability to know ourselves, to recognize those situations where we become stressed out, and to calm our own stress (even if it isn't right in that moment). Sometimes this means that we excuse ourselves from an interaction with our child that isn't going well and, preferably, hand off the situation to another emotionally available adult. Sometimes it means that we seek additional support for ourselves so we can understand more about our own patterns, feelings, and needs. The keys are self-reflection and a willingness to reconnect with our children after there has been a disconnection. If our parents had this ability and modeled these behaviors for us, we have a good start. If our parents were reactive and unaware of themselves and how their actions affected others, we have extra work to do to parent consciously.

Once, I was traveling across the country on a plane and heard the sound of a very distressed baby. I looked around until I found the infant and mother. Mom was frantically bouncing her infant in her arms and shushing the baby. She was clearly distressed, not wanting to bother anyone else on the airplane with her upset baby. I'm sure she knew that she was stressed and that her baby was stressed, but she didn't know the secret to getting her baby to calm: she needed to calm herself. Babies are very sensitive to our stress, so when we, as parents, are stressed because of something that the baby is doing or because of something else unrelated to the baby, our babies will often express those feelings for us. Interesting, huh? If the mom on the plane had recognized that she was feeling stressed and worked to calm herself down, she would probably have calmed her baby.

For this mother, connection might have meant simply acknowledging that she was feeling stressed because her baby was crying and making a lot of noise. If she could have first connected to how she was feeling, she might have then been able to ask herself if her baby was feeling the same way. Connecting with someone else who could just be with her and her feelings of worry might have been all she needed to calm her own nervous system. And if she were to calm her own nervous system, her baby would also become calm. If this mother always struggled with air travel and became upset every time she flew, with or without a baby, she might have considered doing some work of her own on this topic. My series "Changing Your Life's Story" details several ways to work on the origin of our own stress patterns. By prompting Mom to look carefully at herself, the baby may have been doing her a favor.

Overwhelming parenting experiences are windows into our own childhood and what happened to us when we were growing up—experiences that are still affecting us (and our ability to regulate). Our children are here to help us heal from our childhood wounds, and it is their job to subconsciously bring our issues, sensitivities, and pain into the light in order to be healed. And they do a really great job! Parenting has a way of bringing our own early experiences into the light in a way that nothing else can. If we have a strong reaction to our baby's or young child's behavior, something that happened to us as a child is probably coming to the surface.

If you were left to cry, for example, you may feel a strong urge to protect your baby from being left alone. Or you may have been desensitized, feeling that being left to cry didn't hurt you, and so you don't see any harm in leaving your baby alone. You may find that your baby's cries don't really bother you. (Make no mistake—an infant's cries are meant to arouse attention from caregivers and should never be ignored. You *cannot* spoil a baby in the sense that most people understand spoiling. *Spoil* literally means to "leave on the shelf." Babies who are left alone and whose early needs go unmet are those who are truly spoiled.)

Becoming aware of our reactions and their triggers can be wonderful opportunities to learn more about ourselves. On the other hand, when we aren't aware of ourselves and why we are feeling what we feel, we are likely to blame our children when we start having strong feelings. We can view our children as button pushers, or we can view them as providing opportunities for us to heal. It is our choice.

The Relationship Between Parenting Partners: Making Sure You're on the Same Page

How well parents get along and agree on the way they parent has a profound impact on children. Parental interactions show children the way relationships should be, for better or for worse. Seeing how parents and other adults interact creates templates, or road maps, in children's brains that have a strong influence over all of their future relationships, including what kinds of people they marry and how they expect to be treated by their spouse. Parents model the way life is, and when we have children of our own, we will unconsciously recreate our parents' example unless we consciously decide not to follow their patterns.

Parenting is full of major and minor decisions that impact our children, and things work much more smoothly when we have a parenting *partner*. The way each parent was raised is the template for how each parent believes children are to be treated. When two parents' templates basically match, things tend to go smoothly. When their templates disagree, it creates stress and conflict—not an optimal environment for raising children, who are dependent upon our ability to be present and help them learn to regulate their feelings. Parenting partners who are in conflict over parenting decisions are not in a position to make the best choices for anyone.

Chapter One

In an ideal situation, parents will discuss with each other their own childhood experiences before they become parents, read neuroscience-based information about parenting decisions together, and work together to make decisions that will support their children's optimal development. But in the real world, sometimes conflicts don't even become apparent until after a child has joined the family. And even among somewhat enlightened couples, there may be situations that surprise one parent or the other. It is very common for one parent, usually the mother, to educate herself and start to make decisions about parenting. The parent who has not been reading, usually the father, can start to feel like he is making the wrong parenting choices, but not know what he is supposed to do differently.

It is important that parenting partners make the effort to get on the same page, reduce stress and conflict in their relationship with each other, and create a parenting partnership dedicated to raising healthy children. Through the inevitable challenges of parenting we have the opportunity to connect more deeply with our partner, as well as our children. Parenting is a journey, and the path is rarely smooth. Hold on to each other and support each other, and the ride will be much easier.

Samantha and Lane both came from families where there had been a lot of trauma and chaos. When they decided to start a family, they were very aware that they could encounter some significant challenges along the way. Their first child, Elana, was colicky and challenged her parents' collective resources because she cried most of the time and rarely slept. However, because Samantha and Lane were able to talk about how they felt about parenting their daughter, they were actually strengthening their relationship with one another through the adversity.

Samantha and Lane knew that the first step to getting on the same page was understanding and respecting that we each come into parenting with our own set of early experiences, or our own stories, which influence the decisions and feelings we have.

Often, we are not conscious of these feelings, and our feelings may not even be logical. It is usually much easier to see what our partner is expressing than it may be to see our own role in the situation. When we start by working to understand how our partners' experiences lead to the conclusions they are making, we are much closer to getting on the same page than when we come in and try to tell them we just read a great book and are now going to do things differently. Share your thoughts and ideas, then listen to your partner's response to the information. In this process, you will learn more about your partner's beliefs and attitudes. When someone feels heard, he or she is much more likely to take in new information rather than react defensively.

If possible, before you have children, come up with a plan for how you and your partner will handle any disagreements about parenting decisions. Plan regular meetings to discuss how you feel things are going with your children and how each of you feels about parenting, so that small situations don't become big disputes.

I highly recommend taking a parenting class together and discussing what you learn. The Consciously Parenting Project offers classes for couples, both over the phone and on-demand, and your parenting partner can always take the class with you for free.

Sometimes when parents are not on the same page, parenting consultations and/or therapy can be beneficial. There are times when one parent needs support during important conversations, and outside support can help everyone get on the same parenting page again. A consultation with someone who is very familiar with what you are working towards in your parenting and who is able to support both partners is ideal. In-person or phone consultations have made such a difference with many of my clients. I really respect parents who make the effort to get on the phone or Skype together or meet in person to discuss what is really going on and where they are stuck. For these families, being able to talk with an objective listener, who values each family member's needs, creates the safety needed to start to connect again.

The best tool I've seen for parents and partners to connect more deeply with one another is Hedy Schleifer's Crossing the Bridge. (http://www.hedyyumi.com) Whether couples have a good connection with each other and want to support each other on a particular issue or if a much deeper conflict about their relationship or parenting exists, Crossing the Bridge is a valuable way to move out of the old patterns and create connection in the partnership. As discussed in Book I, *Consciously Parenting*, a partner can be the place for the deepest healing to happen and that has ripples into your parenting. When I have partners who are willing to visit the world of the other, I know that any parenting challenge they are having will be resolved because there is a strong foundation between the parents. When the foundation isn't strong, it is best to work on creating more connection between the parents/partners before we move any further into what is happening with the children.

(Note: For those parents without partners, Crossing the Bridge can still be a tool you can use to support your own journey if you have a willing friend or relative open to learning the process.)

Questions to Ponder

Here are some questions you and your parenting partner can talk about before your child joins your family, or at any point you're ready to consciously create relationships with your children.

If you don't have a parenting partner, you can use these discussion questions to jumpstart a conversation with your friends or others in your support network.

- What did your parents do that you remember positively and would like to repeat with your own children?

- What did your parents do that you remember negatively and would like to do differently with your own children?

- What are the needs of children? What do parents do to meet those needs?

- What are the needs of parents? How do parents meet those needs?

- How do you feel about being a parent? What's the hardest thing about parenting? What do you love the most?

Chapter Two

Conscious Conception, Pregnancy and Birth

Conscious Conception

When there has been preparation prior to conception, families are off to a much better start in creating connection. In many primitive cultures, couples begin preparing for a new baby more than a year before they try to conceive. Not only do they eat certain foods known to positively affect fertility and help them conceive a healthy child, but they also create the emotional space for the new child to be welcomed into the entire community. These people make themselves ready on every level to welcome a child.

In modern American society, our lives tend to be devoid of rituals that set our intentions and guide our paths. If you are planning to add a child to your family, consider creating a ritual with your family to create the physical and emotional space in your life for a new child to enter. Some parents-to-be simply light a candle and say a blessing for the baby who will join them and for their growing family.

Another way to prepare for conception is to find, in advance, health-care professionals to support your physical, mental, and emotional concerns about conception, pregnancy, and adding a child to your family. In my case, I had to look until I found someone who could hear and understand what was important to me. When my husband and I decided we were ready to conceive our first child, I called my doctor's office to schedule an appointment to discuss this life transition. I was practically laughed at by the receptionist who couldn't understand why I wanted an appointment and wanted to know if I knew what to do to conceive a baby. "You just start trying," she told me. I made an appointment anyway, only to wait for an hour and a half without seeing the doctor, who was called away to deliver a baby at the last moment.

A few days later, a friend gave me a book about having a baby with a midwife. After reading it from cover to cover, I realized that a midwife might be a better match for me than an obstetrician. (Note: There are obstetricians who have the heart of a midwife, which I discovered later on my journey. This book just helped me to define what I was looking for in a provider.) I was interested enough to call a local birth center, and I talked for over thirty minutes with the midwife who happened to answer the phone. This woman took my concerns seriously and suggested I come in to speak with the head midwife, Debbie Marin. I eventually did become pregnant, and Debbie was the midwife who attended my first child's birth.

I'm not saying it is essential for you to have a midwife; rather, I'm saying it is important that the caregivers you surround yourself with during this time of your life have the heart that my midwife did. Find someone you feel comfortable with, who can answer your questions, and who takes the time to be with you and your partner even before conception. This kind of person will be able to be with you and support you while you are going through the changes of pregnancy, the labor of birth, and the transition into parenthood.

Unplanned Pregnancy

Obviously, it is not always possible to plan every pregnancy, nor is it always possible for parents to be excited about having a baby when they weren't expecting to become pregnant.

When an unexpected pregnancy occurs and the parents feel disappointed by the news, the child feels some rejection, even if the parents' negative reactions to the conception occur only very early on in the pregnancy. Awareness can make a great deal of difference for both parents and children. It is important for parents to acknowledge any feelings that come up about the unanticipated conception and not just sweep the feelings under the rug. Our baby feels rejection even if we think we have "gotten over it" or "moved on." If we're emotionally stuck, our relationship with our future child can suffer due to the lack of connection. Unresolved feelings from the beginning of life with our child can cause a ripple effect in our relationship well after birth, until we can find true peace.

Here are two examples of moms who had unexpected pregnancies and what happened to their relationships with their babies during the first two years.

Lori was married with three children and did not intend to have any more. When Lori unexpectedly found that she was pregnant, she and her husband, Jim, were both completely shocked. They decided that there was nothing they could do about it, since abortion was not an option for them, and settled into doing what had to be done. They made regular prenatal visits to the doctor, and Lori stopped drinking and smoking. They planned their hospital birth and prepared to feed the new baby formula, since it would be less inconvenient than breast-feeding. Once he was born, they felt their baby, Aaron, was an inconvenience and expressed those feelings in most of their interactions with him. Even though they did their best to meet what they understood his needs to be (Aaron was always fed, his diaper was changed when dirty, and he was held occasionally), they were emotionally detached from Aaron.

Lori was diagnosed with post-partum depression three months after giving birth. Aaron showed signs of depression, as well, including sleeping a lot and reduced eye contact with his parents. Jim and Lori frequently misread Aaron's cues about his needs; for example, when Aaron needed to be held, they instead put him to bed, thinking he must be tired. As early as possible, Aaron was encouraged to be more independent than he was capable of being. Lori and Jim frequently left him crying in his crib so that he would learn to put himself to sleep, but they also left him to cry when they were caring for other children or when they were tired. At one year, Aaron was assessed and found to have an avoidant attachment with his mother and a disorganized attachment with his father. Lori and Jim never managed to come to terms with their feelings about having an unexpected baby. They cared for Aaron's most basic needs, but there was always a level of resentment toward him and his dependency needs. This pattern that started at the beginning defined the course of their relationship.

In contrast to Lori and Jim, Andrea was unmarried, living with Bob when she discovered she was expecting a baby. Bob was very upset, as he didn't want any children, and Andrea was upset because Bob was not supportive. She spent lots of time writing about her feelings about the baby and about the relationship she was in. As she expressed her feelings in her journal and spoke with her supportive friends, she was able to come to peace with having another baby. She decided to marry Bob, who softened about having the baby, and the three of them had a connected birthing experience. (See the birth section later in this chapter for more information on creating a connected birthing experience.) Andrea bonded with the new baby, Robby, by holding him frequently, breastfeeding, and fully accepting the gift of Robby in her life. Bob fell in love with his son, and in caring for him regularly by changing diapers, bathing him, rocking him, and going for walks outside with him, he realized that he was capable of becoming a loving father. He embraced his role as father to Robby.

Bob and Andrea had flexible jobs where Robby could go to work with one of them every day, so he was cared for daily by his parents. Andrea and Bob were both very attentive and attuned to Robby's needs. Life was not always easy, but the connection between Andrea and Robby was palpable, as was the connection between Bob and Robby. At eighteen months old, Robby was advanced in his verbal communication, with a large (seventy-five-plus word) vocabulary. Despite the rocky beginning, Andrea and Bob's efforts to express and come to terms with their feelings about Robby's unexpected conception clearly paid off in the form of a secure attachment between Baby and Mom, and Dad and Baby.

In both of these examples, the pregnancies were unplanned and not initially welcomed, but the parents developed very different relationships with their children after birth because of the emotional preparation that each family did or didn't do. When parents are able to find a sense of peace about an unexpected pregnancy, there is emotional space for connection. When we release our resentment about someone or some situation in our lives, we create room in our lives for new blessings to enter.

Finding Peace with an Unplanned Pregnancy (for Both Moms and Dads)

Whether you are currently faced with an unplanned pregnancy or you now have an older child whose conception wasn't expected, the following information is for you. If you feel anger, sadness, or regrets regarding a pregnancy or child, it is essential that you work through those thoughts and feelings.

One way to do so is to write about them, using the following questions as prompts. You can also answer these questions aloud with a friend or your parenting partner, if he or she is able to simply listen to you process your feelings without trying to change or fix how you feel. One suggestion is to request that the person listening to you simply repeat back what they heard you share. See *Crossing the Bridge,* by Hedy and Yumi Schleifer, in the resources section for more information about using this process.

1. When did you first learn of the pregnancy? What were your thoughts and feelings about the new baby coming into your life?

2. What thoughts and feelings did you have as you went through the pregnancy? What decisions did you make regarding your baby? Were the thoughts creating connection or moving toward peace? Or were your thoughts creating disconnection?

3. Write about your baby's birth. What were you thinking and feeling as you anticipated your baby's arrival? What was it like when you saw the baby for the first time?

Here are some more things you can you do to work through your feelings and connect with your child.

If you're still pregnant:

- Find a close friend or birth-support person (a doula, childbirth educator, or midwife, for example) who can listen to you without trying to fix the situation or offer advice.

- Find a therapist who specializes in supporting pregnant partners.

- Talk to your partner honestly about how you're feeling, allowing yourself to move through whatever you're feeling without judging yourself.

- Talk to your unborn baby about your feelings. The baby feels them whether you acknowledge those feelings or not.

If you've recently given birth:

- Talk to your baby about your feelings. Cry with your baby.

- Find a perinatal psychology specialist who can guide your process. (See the resources at the back of the book for suggestions.)

If your child is older:

- If appropriate, talk with your child and let her know how you felt when you learned you were pregnant (for example, you felt not ready to be a parent, you felt surprised).

Reassure her that your feelings were about you, not her. Take responsibility for how she must have felt and probably still feels.

- Tell your child that he is worthy and wanted, and you're so glad that he came into your life. This reassurance alone can go a long way toward healing your relationship!

Conscious Pregnancy

Whether a baby's conception was carefully planned or a complete surprise, moms can give their babies a healthy emotional start by reducing their stress and taking care of themselves during pregnancy. In fact, doing both is vital to your baby's emotional health and your relationship with your baby. If you had a stressful pregnancy with your child, this is another opportunity to remember that you did the best you could with the information you had at the time. Release your guilt!

Stress and the Developing Baby

Stress affects a developing baby and can affect the baby's ability to be calm or soothed after birth. This includes stress from work, stress from your marriage or partner, and stress about the pregnancy itself. When we are experiencing stress, our bodies release stress hormones to prepare us to fight or run away. In the world we live in, stress is everywhere, so we need to be especially mindful of our choices and our environment when we are expecting a baby. The baby doesn't care about the origin of the stress, only that it is present. Stress during pregnancy can prime the baby's physiological system, and specifically the nervous system, for being born into a potentially hostile environment. When we make the effort to keep our stress in check in our own lives, we are making an investment in our baby's overall health.

Low stress during pregnancy, according to Peter Levine in his book *Trauma Through a Child's Eyes,* creates grooves in neural pathways (the communication system in our brain) for deep relaxation and self-soothing, and gives the baby the capacity to tolerate stress and frustration. Stress is much more than just an experience that has a negative effect; it actually lays down the wiring of the baby's developing brain, says Bruce Perry, an internationally-recognized authority on childhood trauma and the brain. It is possible to later change the wiring through experience, but changing unhelpful wiring is much more difficult than creating optimal wiring in the first place.

During pregnancy, the baby's brain develops from the bottom to the top, from the base of the brain (the brain stem, where our body's automatic systems, such as breathing and heart rate, are regulated) to the emotional part of the brain (including the amygdala, or fear receptor of the brain, which is located next to the brain stem) and finally to the cortex (the higher-thinking part of the brain, positioned above the eyes and behind the forehead). (See Figure 1, right.) While the parts of the brain responsible for conscious memories do not develop until well into a child's third year of life, the part of the brain responsible for unconscious memories is working during pregnancy. That means anything a mother experiences when she is pregnant, the baby experiences, too—and the memory of that experience is stored in the unborn baby's brain and body.

A story I heard from a loving parent who adopted a baby boy at birth really drove home this point for me. When the boy, Harvey, was about two years old, he started spontaneously screaming words that, according to his mother, he had never heard before. Harvey was home with his mom, Karen, all day; he had never been to daycare and didn't watch television. Their lives were rhythmic and relatively quiet. Karen and her husband, Larry, had a stable marriage where there was no yelling. So when Harvey yelled, "I'm gonna kill you!" Karen was shocked. He didn't just say it like some children repeat something they've heard; he said it with a deep voice that sent chills down Karen's spine. Karen knew that Harvey's birth mother had been threatened by his birth father during the entire pregnancy, and Harvey would have heard those words in utero. Even though Harvey had no conscious memories of his birth father, he had clearly brought some interactions with him into his new life.

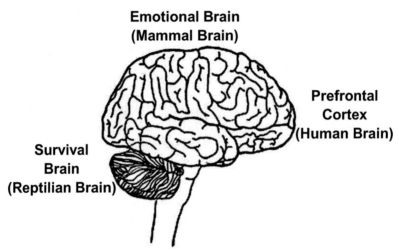

Figure 1: The Brain.

If you are experiencing lots of stress during your pregnancy, do what you can to decrease it. Small changes now can have a huge impact on your child's developing brain and nervous system. When you do experience stress, talk to your unborn baby about it, letting him know that it isn't about him and that you're going to do your best to keep things calm. Connect with your baby daily and do something soothing for both of you, such as reading a story that makes you smile, humming a favorite tune, or taking a walk in nature. The most important thing with this activity is that *you* enjoy doing it, because your baby will feel your joy.

Mothering the Mother

Self-care for pregnant moms is a big part of reducing stress. Growing a baby is hard work, and this work isn't honored as much as it needs to be in our modern American society. In our society, we rarely slow down to rest in the best or the worst of times. We feel we need to be doing and going all the time. Pregnancy is definitely a time to slow down, to create a nest for yourself and your new family, to honor the transition into parenthood.

Many mothers feel like they need to prove that they can handle everything in their lives as well as being pregnant, and they don't create the space for resting and listening to their bodies during pregnancy. As we women transition into motherhood, it is really important that we learn to listen to our bodies, for it is by connecting with ourselves and with our own bodies that we connect with our baby. Rest when you're tired. Eat when you're hungry. Exercise when your body needs to move. Being active, especially doing nurturing activities, is good for a pregnant mom's changing body. Striving to find the balance between rest and activity during pregnancy is a good exercise for a mom's new life to come.

If you're an expectant mom, surround yourself with support people who can nurture you during your pregnancy. This doesn't mean hibernating or having others wait on you hand and foot (although some of that service is very, very nice). It just means enlisting the help of friends and your parenting partner to help you take good care of yourself and ensure you're taking lots of time to be pampered and to relax. These nurturing people can include your obstetrician, midwife, or doula (a woman specifically trained to support moms before, during, and after childbirth), as well as your friends and family. Learn to ask for what you need during this time.

Consider creating a group for expectant mothers or join one in your area so that you can all support one another during this transition to parenthood. If partners are included in this group, even better, because you will be parents together, and we often forget that dads need support, too. La Leche League and Attachment Parenting International are just two of the organizations that offer support groups for parents around the world. These organizations are great places to ask questions, as well as to hear other parents asking questions you might not have thought to ask. The advice from these organizations is generally in line with the current research on attachment and the philosophy of parenting in a gentle way in the early years. However, as with anyone's advice, if something you hear doesn't feel right to you, take what does work for you and leave the rest behind.

Nutrition During Pregnancy

There is never a time when what you eat matters more than the time before, during, and after pregnancy. This is the time when your body requires the most nutrients to grow your baby. When you take good care of both your emotional and physical needs, you will have a healthier baby.

Fats, something that most of us have learned to dread and loathe, are incredibly important during pregnancy. A baby's brain is composed primarily of fat, and healthy fats actually help lay down a baby's brain structure. This structure, in turn, impacts the building of neural pathways and, thus, emotional health. Examples of healthy fats include those found in avocados and nuts (especially soaked and sprouted nuts and seeds), as well as the fat found in grass-fed cheese, in other raw or gently pasteurized grass-fed dairy products, and meat broths (chicken, fish, or beef) from healthy animals. Pregnancy isn't a license to go out and eat as much fatty food as possible, however. Not all fats are created equal; make sure you learn to distinguish healthy from harmful fats and fat sources.

In addition to raw fruits and vegetables, there are many whole foods that support the growth of a healthy baby. Check out the book *Nourishing Traditions* by Sally Fallon (listed in the resources section) for recipe ideas for nourishing whole foods. Some foods recommended in this book, like organ meats, aren't for the faint of heart, but the book's recipes come from traditional societies around the world that have been found to have the healthiest people.

Many chemicals in our food, including monosodium glutamate (best known as MSG, but which has many different names on food labels), adversely affect a baby's development. Highly processed foods, so common today that we sometimes don't even realize how far away from nature they are, are best avoided or limited. A farmer friend of mine, Dennis Stoltzfoos, once told me that if we can't imagine a particular food growing in a field, hanging on a tree, or growing in a garden, we probably don't need to eat it. While most of us probably won't go to that extreme, it is a good rule of thumb to keep in mind.

Due to factory farming, our meat is not as healthy as we've been led to believe by manufacturers. We need to learn more about the way animals are treated so that we can make informed decisions regarding what we are putting into our bodies, especially during pregnancy, because these foods are forming our children's bodies. Animals that are allowed to forage, have access to the outdoors, and are eating appropriate foods for that animal (hint: most animals were not designed to eat corn) are much healthier overall. Research has shown that meat from grass-fed and grass-finished animals is higher in omega 3 fatty acids than animals fed corn. Meat from grass-fed animals is also much lower in saturated fat than meat from corn-fattened animals who spent their lives confined without light or fresh air or who spend the end of their lives in a feedlot in close quarters, just eating—all of which makes animals sick. It has become challenging to find meat animals treated as they were meant to be treated.

Consider checking out the Weston A. Price Foundation for information on traditional whole-food nutrition. Weston Price was a dentist in the 1930s and 1940s, and after seeing awful tooth decay in his Ohio practice, he searched for a diet that would lead to healthy teeth. Price's work looked at primitive societies at the point where "foods of modern commerce" entered the scene. What he found was that the primitive foods were very high in many nutrients not present in the other "modern" foods. Even more striking were the differences in infants and children who were fed traditional whole foods instead of newer foods. His book *Nutrition and Physical Degeneration* is eye opening and full of examples of the differences he found by looking only at a society's dietary changes. He found that the health of the mouth reflected the health of the body as a whole and that the diet he thought would be healthiest, a vegetarian diet, wasn't the healthiest after all. Diet affected everything from a person's disposition as a child and adult to women's ability to have a natural birth.

The Price-Pottenger Nutrition Foundation also has a book entitled *For Tomorrow's Children*. The book offers nutritional advice, describing what both parents (not just the mother) can eat before pregnancy for the optimal health of their future baby, as well as the best foods for pregnant and breastfeeding moms and their babies.

Conscious Birth

Birth is our first experience with the outside world, and those experiences we have during birth and in the first hour or so after birth have a powerful impact on the way we subconsciously view the world. We are meant to enter the world as an active participant in our own birth, yet when we are under the influence of drugs given to our mothers to dull or eliminate labor pain, we are unable to do that effectively. When we are pulled out of the womb with forceps or via caesarian section (C-section), we no longer have the same active role that we were biologically designed to have. The more interventions that are used during our birth, the more likely we will experience a birth trauma.

When we have a shock to our nervous system during the birthing process, it activates the fight, flight, or freeze response in the brain. We may become a baby who is unable to effectively establish a relationship with our mother because we are overwhelmed from the shock of what has happened. Many times, babies become very fussy after such insults, and that fussiness further challenges new parents to connect with their babies in a meaningful way. The more birth is allowed to unfold naturally and the more the birth team can support the mother in listening to her own body during labor, the easier and more peaceful birth will be for everyone.

Medically assisted hospital birth has been the norm for only about sixty years. Prior to that, the norm was to have babies at home, without medical intervention. My grandmother, who just celebrated her one-hundredth birthday, was born at home and had half of her children, including twins, at home. Women have forgotten that our bodies inherently know how to give birth, partially because we've been told that we can't do it without the help of drugs or doctors. If your inner guidance says you can have your baby naturally, without the aid of drugs or interventions such as C-sections, chances are very high that you'll be able to do just that, especially if you have a support team dedicated to helping you reach that goal.

Make sure you feel safe in the location where you will give birth. The location you choose can have a great deal to do with whether or not you have a natural birth. For example, western European countries such as the Netherlands, where the majority of care for pregnant women and birth is provided by midwives, have a low rate of interventions because midwives are trained to handle most situations in a way that supports the mother and the baby. Midwives are specialists in normal births, and by providing emotional support for a woman in labor, they are able to help women avoid many of the common interventions used now when giving birth. In these countries, only high-risk mothers are cared for by obstetricians, since high-risk moms are more likely to need the specialty services offered by such providers.

In the United States, the costs for childbirth are among the highest in the world, yet infant mortality rates, as well as maternal mortality rates, are also among the highest. Other countries with lower birth costs and far fewer interventions have much better infant and maternal mortality rates—the measures that matter the most. Perhaps we can learn from these other countries, even if we can apply the lessons only to our own birthing decisions.

Making an informed decision about the location of your birth might mean looking at your local hospitals to see if they have the "Mother Friendly" or "Baby Friendly" designation. These designations mean that the institutions have followed criteria created by the World Health Organization and UNICEF for birthing and breastfeeding practices that support the health of the baby, including keeping mothers and babies together after birth whenever possible, initiating early breastfeeding, and providing breastfeeding support. Choosing the right location for you might mean looking at birthing centers in hospitals or at free-standing birth centers that are run by midwives. In many states, home birth is also an option.

Choose a birth team you trust, and include individuals who share your desire to keep the birth as natural as possible. A birth team can include midwives, doulas, nurse midwives, obstetricians, or any combination of these (for example, a midwife and doula, or an obstetrician assisted by midwives), depending upon your unique needs and situation. Family members—perhaps your husband or partner, or your mother, grandmother, sister, or close friend—can also be a part of your birth team. The most important part of choosing a birth team is making sure you are comfortable with the people who will be with you as you bring your baby into the world.

Doulas can be wonderful assets regardless of the birth setting, because they are dedicated to supporting you and your birth, and they can advocate for you to have the kind of birth you want. The more educated you are as the mother, the more likely you will find an arrangement that works for you and your family and that supports the goal of having the most natural birth possible.

Risk Factors for Shock During Birth

- Stress in the mother, the partner, the parental relationship during pregnancy
- Preterm labor
- Induction of labor
- Hospital birth
- Epidural or other pain medication
- C-section delivery
- Forceps used during delivery
- Vacuum extraction
- Fear (conscious or unconscious, Mom's and/or the baby's) during labor, birth, or postpartum
- Suctioning
- Cord clamping before cord stops pulsing
- Mother and baby being separated for any reason
- NICU visit
- Circumcision

Birth Trauma

Birth trauma is very real. It deeply affects both mothers and babies, and depending upon what happened, Mom (as well as

Dad and the baby, too) may need additional support to work through the trauma.

If things don't go well during labor, it is important that you take the time after it is over to express your thoughts and feelings about what happened. Address your expectations and create an understanding of your experience. Find people who can listen to you while you express your thoughts and feelings. One of the biggest, most supportive experiences I had after my baby died was when my midwife, Jennifer, came to visit me about a month later. We were able to talk through the birth, including what she saw and what went through her head, and I was able to talk about my experience of the birth. Her counsel was especially helpful because Jennifer had lost a baby herself and understood what I was going through. We cried together and openly talked about the experience. Talking with her didn't end my work of releasing this birth trauma, but it was an important step in my healing process.

Birth trauma is often minimized by well-meaning people who say things like, "Well, you both survived," "All that matters is that the baby is healthy," or "It could have been worse. Let me tell you about *my* birth." If you're upset by the way your birth went, you have a right to express your feelings about how it felt to *you*. Even if everything went "well" according to your doctor or your mother, if *you* feel disappointed about even one part, it is important. And if it was overwhelming for you, I guarantee it was overwhelming for your baby. It is important that you create a healing space for yourself so that you can then support your baby to heal from the experience.

Many feel that birth trauma doesn't matter to babies because they believe babies can't remember what happened. As mentioned earlier, the part of the brain responsible for unconscious memories is fully developed and working by the time a baby is born. Although babies may not consciously re-member trauma associated with their births, they do remember it unconsciously, and birth trauma affects the baby's nervous system. When a baby experiences something overwhelming before, during, or after birth, the baby's autonomic nervous system experiences a shock. When there has been a shock to the nervous system, the body is flooded with the three adrenal stress hormones: cortisol, DHEA, and adrenaline. Babies are unable to regulate their own stress and, through their behavior, will begin to show signs of the distress they're experiencing within their bodies. For example, a baby who isn't sleeping well may be in a shock state from an earlier overwhelming experience. If we aren't aware of this underlying reason for her "fussiness," we can begin to think that we have a high-need baby and not give her the support she needs. The experiences surrounding birth have a profound impact on our bodies, minds, and nervous systems, affecting our beliefs about ourselves in ways that may never be fully understood.

The cells of the baby's body will also remember birth trauma, even if the child doesn't remember it in the traditional cognitive sense later in life. Bruce Lipton's work on cellular memory holds some interesting keys to understanding why cells hold onto trauma. In his book *The Biology of Belief,* he discusses the fact that we spend the first two years of our lives primarily in the delta brain-wave state and from ages two to six primarily in the theta brain-wave state. When I trained as a hypnotherapist, I learned to relax a client back into delta or theta brain-wave states because in those states, a client is more suggestible. Children don't consistently have alpha brain-wave activity until they are about six years old, which means that they aren't able to consistently have conscious thoughts and make conscious decisions before that time. Because they are in the suggestible delta and theta brain-wave states, everything that happens to them or around them is taken in as fact. And everything they learn during their first six years of life is stored in their subconscious mind because they don't have the ability to decide if they want to keep it or not. They cannot tell themselves, for example, that what is happening in a particular situation is not how things normally happen because they don't yet know how things normally happen. Those circumstances then become the lens through which they view the world.

Sometimes, despite the best of intentions, the birth we wanted doesn't happen. What can parents do to help ease the shock of an overwhelming event for themselves and the baby? If medical interventions are necessary during your child's birth, or there was an overwhelming event of some kind during the birth or the postpartum period, spend lots of time with your baby (after you have worked through some of your own feelings about what happened), talking to him about how scary (sad, frustrating, or otherwise upsetting) it was. Just support your baby's feelings, allowing him to discharge the feelings in your arms and join him in expressing his experience of what happened. Hold your baby as much as possible, skin-to-skin, and be extra good to yourself. Many of the attachment-parenting suggestions given in the following chapters are good for all babies, but they are especially good when there has been a birth trauma. Relationships involving connection and physical touch are all very healing for everyone, including the baby.

As you calm your own nervous system from an adverse birth experience, your baby will calm, too. You and your baby are inextricably linked. Parenting partners need to support Mom as much as possible during this time, keeping everyone's stress levels very low and creating a space to share what happened.

The nonprofit organization Building and Enhancing Bonding and Attachment (BEBA) and Ray Castellino and Mary Jackson of About Connections in Santa Barbara, California, has been doing clinical research in all aspects of family connection, starting as early in pregnancy as possible, for nearly twenty years. What they've found is that babies show the stories of their births from the time they are born, but most parents don't understand what the baby is trying to show them. Babies need their parents to recognize that they are showing the story of how they experienced their births. When we can slow down and create the space to connect with our babies about their births, one of the biggest events in both babies' and parents' lives, as well as the smaller and more mundane aspects of daily life, we connect deeply with our children while we integrate our experiences. Parents also need the space to share their birth stories, not only with each other, but with their babies as well.

Brain-wave State Primer

The brains of adults and children are not just different because a child's brain is smaller or less well developed. Structurally, a child's brain functions differently than an adult's brain until around puberty. Brain-wave states, or states of consciousness, can be measured using an EEG and are measured in cycles per second.

Delta. (0.5-4 cycles per second) For an adult, delta is a deep sleep. For infants and toddlers up to age 2, this is the brain-wave state during sleeping and waking. Babies and toddlers are learning in this state, whether they appear to be awake or asleep and require no repetitions to learn in this state. Subconscious mind, cellular memory record what happens effortlessly in delta.

Theta. (4-8 cycles per second) An adult is in a deep meditative state or asleep in the theta brain-wave state. Adults can access their intuition and creativity in this state. Children between the ages of 2-6 are generally in this state of consciousness and learn through imitation as they absorb what is happening to them and around them.

(continued)

Alpha. (8-12 cycles per second) An adult in alpha would be in a relaxed awake state, as when walking in nature, playing music, knitting, or in a light sleep state. Children between the ages of 7 and 14 speed up to alpha and are more predominantly in the emotional parts of their brains than the conscious, rational areas.

Beta. (13-30 cycles per second) Beta is the go, go, go, do, do, do brain-wave state. As adults, this is where we spend the majority of our time. It is where we think things through and are alert and active. Children do not reach this brain-wave state as their primary state of consciousness until around age 14. In the beta brain-wave state, we require thousands of repetitions to learn something new.

Using the clinical research by Castellino and Jackson, I've been helping families connect and integrate early experiences for the past two years. I've been amazed at the shifts that happen in families as they realize that each person in the family, no matter how small, is trying to communicate with one another and be heard. When the space is made for everyone to connect and share his or her stories, the challenges that brought them to see me often resolve. These families have shown me the power of creating a sacred space and that no child is too young to have a story to tell. As I reflect back on my first child's birth and first year, I strongly suspect that our breastfeeding, colic, and sleep challenges were all part of my son's expression of his overwhelming prenatal and birth experiences that I didn't understand at the time. I wonder how different things could have been if I had been able to listen to his story instead of just focusing on my desired outcome (a baby who wasn't fussy, had an easy time breastfeeding, and slept well). If you're interested in learning more about

Ray Castellino and Mary Jackson's work, please check out our "Little People, Big Challenges" audio programs. (www.consciouslyparenting.com/LPBC)

Hospital Birth and Shock

Hospitals have become a normal part of birthing in our culture. I want to honor the safety many families feel when birthing in a hospital setting, knowing that life-saving measures are readily available if they're needed. I've also heard of situations where a family is planning a homebirth and the mother decides that the baby needs to be born in a hospital only to discover that there was a medical issue with the baby. Birth needs to happen where everyone feels the safest.

That said, families delivering in hospitals are more likely to be subjected to unnecessary interventions than families birthing in out-of-hospital settings. Sometimes these interventions are necessary and life-saving. Other times, interventions are iatrogenic, or cause problems that wouldn't have otherwise been an issue. For example, women are often advised to have labor induced, but often the risks of induction are not clearly discussed. Once an induction has been started, mother and baby are frequently in for a cascade of interventions until the baby is born. Beginning by stripping the membranes, rupturing membranes, or Pitocin, if labor doesn't progress according to the hospital time-table, more interventions will be added to speed it along unnaturally. Each intervention increases the likelihood of a C-section.

(continued)

To be clear, there are times when the risk of induction and other interventions are outweighed by the risks of continuing the pregnancy, but the fact that interventions affect the baby, the mother-baby, and the early relationship is often minimized because there isn't an immediate apparent effect.

- If the baby isn't ready to be born (labor hasn't started spontaneously) and labor is induced, it is a shock to the baby's nervous system.

- If the mother is worried, scared, terrified because of what is happening during labor, this is a shock to the baby's nervous system. I've heard many stories from parents about how doctors used fear to convince parents to agree to the next intervention. This fear deeply affects parents and the baby.

- Each subsequent intervention, including the known effects of Pitocin on the baby's nervous system, creates a shock to the baby's immature nervous system and creates an imprint for the baby.

- Pitocin increases the pain felt by the mother during contractions, so most women who are induced end up with either pain medication or an epidural. An epidural increases the risk of labor slowing, thus a higher dose of Pitocin is given to keep contractions going. A higher dose of Pitocin often puts the baby in distress (there is actually a term nurses use

(continued)

> called "Pit to distress," in which they increase the dose of Pitocin until the baby goes into distress and then they decrease it). Distress in the baby increases the likelihood of an emergency C-section.
>
> While shock around birth can certainly be experienced in any setting, the current litigious climate of hospitals makes the cascade of interventions much more likely. In addition, doctors who are trained in handling emergencies in birth are often not trained in normal birth and how to support it. As an example, the hospital where my oldest son was born had a 98% epidural rate. When I gave birth without an epidural, I opened my eyes during transition to find my room filled with people who came to see what a natural birth looked like. It wasn't that they wouldn't support me, it was that they had simply never seen a natural birth.

The Fourth Trimester and "Nine In, Nine Out"

Humans are the only animals that don't walk within a short time after birth. Human babies are born the least mature of all animals and are the most dependent upon their parents for the longest amount of time, yet most parenting advice doesn't take this fact into account. Human infants need time to adjust to life outside the womb, as their immature physical bodies really aren't ready for separation from the mother-baby unit until about a year after conception. Some organizations have embraced the concept of a fourth trimester, in which mothers and babies are in close physical proximity to one another for three months following birth, to allow the babies time to adjust slowly to life outside the womb.

The environment inside the womb is peaceful, but also noisy and full of motion. When the baby is born, everything changes very suddenly. Many parents respect this time of transition and help the baby adjust by wearing the baby in a sling, co-sleeping, and consistently responding to the baby's cues. Many other parents, following typical parenting advice, put their baby in a still, quiet, dark room away from Mom and wonder why the baby doesn't enjoy it. Our babies need to be in close proximity to us, because when our babies are in arms, we are there to help them adjust to the world.

Revisiting "The 5 S's"

While we all have times when we need some suggestions to help calm a fussy baby so that we don't lose our minds, it is important to recognize that transitioning into the world is a big change. Our children need the opportunity to express their feelings with our full presence. When we are constantly trying to soothe our babies, we are communicating that we need them to be quiet and that there isn't room for their expression of feelings. When we are constantly trying to calm them down, we are missing the important safety valve of connecting with our children when they're upset, in distress, or blowing off some steam.

Many parents have found the work of Harvey Karp and his 5 S's to soothe an upset baby to be invaluable. While there is certainly a time for these kinds of techniques, especially when parents are exhausted or a baby is particularly fussy, it is important not to use them in place of allowing your child to express her

(continued)

---

story. When a baby is fussy, there is a reason. Remember that babies are expressing and showing their stories. Techniques like the 5 S's are meant to shut down the baby, and this actually creates an overwhelm in the baby's system. Rather than a calm baby, the baby is now disconnected and dysregulated.

I've found that deep healing can happen in the early days and weeks following birth so that the baby is integrating her story rather than shutting down. Babies who shut down early are often much more difficult later on. When connection happens with a baby, the early unmet needs can be met and the behaviors will change. While it isn't instantaneous, changes that result from connection are long lasting.

If I were going to create my own 5 S's, they'd look something like this:

Support the baby by creating space for feelings and story.

Support the mother's needs to share her birth story and to have her feelings about it, good or bad.

Support the mother by creating space for her to mother her baby.

Support the mother-father unit (or mother-partner unit) to share their birth story with each other.

Support the family unit by having extended family or community members bring food and care for the family's basic needs.

Questions to Ponder

- What do you know about your own conception? Your birth? Your early life? What about your partner's? As a starting point, consider what stories your family shared with you about your early life. You probably know more than you think about your own conception, birth, and early life.

- If you are expecting a baby, how important is it to you to have a natural birth? What are your goals for the birth? What does your baby need?

- If you already have a child, was your child's birth traumatic? Did anything overwhelming happen immediately during the birth, after the birth, or in the first few months, such as a stay in a neonatal intensive care unit (NICU)?

- If you adopted your baby, what do you know about his birth mother's pregnancy or about the baby's birth?

- Regardless what age your child is now, do you feel connected to your child? Do your child's behaviors make sense to you? If you feel disconnected, when did that feeling start? Many times, I find that parents see their baby's birth or another early experience as the point of disconnection. Is that true in your family?

Chapter Three

Creating Connection
in Your Child's First Years

In this chapter, we'll look at what you can do to help your baby achieve optimal development. This is a wonderful chapter to read before your baby is born or comes home because it will help guide your understanding of your child's development and inform your decisions. However, even if your baby is older or you are parenting an older child, this chapter can help you to understand more about your children's early life needs, as well as the needs you had when you were an infant. The kinds of parenting decisions you may have made (or been inclined to make) with your own young children can give you clues about the decisions your parents may have made with you. This understanding is a great place to start your parenting journey. The more you know about yourself, the more conscious your parenting process will become and, thus, the better you'll feel about your day-to-day parenting decisions.

In order to grow optimally, children need much more than care for their physical bodies. They must have physical touch, unconditional love, physical presence, emotional presence, and affection every day. What do these things look like? What bonding behaviors can help parents stay in the green-light state, and connect with their children in the yellow-light moments of the relationship? As you move forward in this chapter, think in terms of these general ideas: warmth, nurturing, rocking, cuddling, smiling, singing, and playing. Are these things part of your parenting repertoire?

If your parenting has not included the types of bonding, connecting actions described here, it is important to release any guilt you may feel when you read about them. This discussion is not meant to make anyone feel guilty, but to foster your understanding of optimal parenting. We all do the best we can with the tools and information we have available to us at any given time. Once we know better, we can do better.

Specific Actions for Creating Connection

In order to grow optimally, our children need us parents to put an incredible amount of energy into parenting in their early years. If we don't spend the time meeting their needs early in our relationships with them, we will need to put in that time later. Fulfilling children's needs later, when the children are older, is not impossible, but it is usually much more challenging for a number of reasons. It requires finding age-appropriate ways to meet the needs of older children whose needs weren't met when they were younger.

When I first became a parent, I used many of the ideas associated with attachment parenting to guide my early decisions. *Attachment parenting,* a term coined by pediatrician William Sears, refers to actions parents can take to create connection with their children, such as responding to their baby's cries, babywearing, sharing sleep or co-sleeping, and breastfeeding. These behaviors felt good to me, allowing me to learn my son's cues and deepen our relationship.

Attachment parenting has been often misunderstood; many people see it as a checklist of things parents must do in order for their child to "attach" to them, rather than as a list of guidelines that can help to foster physical closeness and emotional connection. Consciously parenting takes the ideas of attachment parenting into consideration because they can be the foundation for a solid connection with our children. Neither the attachment-parenting suggestions nor the consciously parenting guiding principles are meant to be a checklist to follow in order to be a "good" parent. If co-sleeping or breastfeeding creates a disconnection in your relationship, continuing to do it while feeling resentful won't create more connection. The goal is to foster a healthy relationship, rather than following someone else's list of what must be done to parent "perfectly."

This chapter will explore all of these bonding behaviors in detail so that you can make an informed decision about what you and your child need, but first, let's look at the different, but equally vital roles mothers and fathers play in attachment parenting.

The Role of the Mother in Consciously Parenting: Nurturing Connection

In consciously parenting, the roles of "mother" and "father" can be played by anyone in a child's life—not just the biological mother or father. Except in the case of breastfeeding, the mother role does not necessarily need to be fulfilled by a woman, nor does the father role need to be filled by a man. For example, there may be a family where the mother role is played by a nurturing grandfather, or perhaps a family includes committed partners of the same sex. Having someone of the male gender in the mother's role or a female in the father's doesn't mean that your child cannot grow to be well adjusted. We just need to understand the value each role plays in meeting the needs of our children.

The mother, who carries the baby in her body for nine months (really ten months) and brings the baby into the world through the birthing process, necessarily has a very important role in the life of the new baby. Babies, at birth, know the sound of their parents' voices and turn toward them. Within twenty-four hours of birth, a newborn can identify his mother's smell. By design, mother and baby are intended to be close to one another. The ideal, as we'll discuss in this chapter, is for a child's own nurturing, biological mother to play the mom role in his or her life. However, we recognize that this isn't always possible.

The mother's primary job is to ease the baby's transition from the womb into the world. Mother acts as an external regulation center for the baby, who has a very immature nervous system at birth. It is through her responsive care that the baby learns to calm herself after something stressful happens. It is through the mother's attunement to the baby's feelings that the child learns what she is feeling. Through mirror neurons, or parts of the emotional brain that match in both mother and baby when they are sharing an emotional experience, such as happiness or sadness, and through her own facial expressions, Mom can show the baby what she is experiencing. Mothers and babies naturally mirror each other's expressions and emotional states when they are playing together. This is called attunement. If your baby is laughing, you will probably laugh, too, and the same parts of the brain are responding in both you and your baby. When you and your baby are both enjoying something funny and then you slowly return yourself to a state of peaceful calm, you teach your baby to do the same.

Having someone else connect with our feelings at this early age is critical to our healthy development. When a new mother is depressed, she is often unable to respond to the baby's cues and connect. As a result, her baby will often show signs of depression, too. (Note: In a case like this, it is important that the mother receives support, and that someone is connecting with the baby in the meantime.)

Infants and their mothers are meant to fall in love with one another and develop an exclusive relationship. Regardless of when you fall in love in your relationship with your child, doing so is a vital part of the relationship-creation process.

The Role of the Father in Consciously Parenting: Play and the Big, Wide World

In consciously parenting, fathers also have an important role in the development of their children. Babies need to have playful interactions and to learn to connect with other people who aren't necessarily as well attuned to their feelings and needs. Most of our experiences in the world are not going to be with others who fully connect, understand and empathize with us, so we need to know we're going to be all right when we encounter these people.

Dad's first role is to support Mom in the first few very intense months after birth, when the baby is all about Mom. My husband, for example, was wonderful about bringing me food, holding our son when I needed a break (or a shower), and changing lots of diapers.

When the baby is ready for more interaction with the world, usually around the end of that fourth trimester discussed in chapter two, it is time for Dad! When we mothers wear our babies, we tend to turn them inward toward us. But a friend of mine noticed that several dads she'd seen wearing their babies in soft carriers had their children facing away from themselves, facing outward to the world. This difference is a perfect analogy for this part of the parenting journey. Dad's job is to add active play into the lives of children. I remember riding on my dad's back around the living room as a child myself. And I joyfully recall the look of delight on my six-month-old son's face as he was being thrown up in the air by my husband in the swimming pool.

The role of the father in consciously parenting is necessarily different than that of the mother, but that doesn't mean that it isn't important. It may take some negotiating for dads to discover their own unique role in parenting their baby, especially if their own father wasn't an involved parent.

Just because we're defining the role of the father here in terms of play doesn't mean that fathers cannot also nurture. In fact, being a nurturer is also an important role. Children need to have a father model for them what it means to be a man who is respectful of others' needs. Some fathers are even the primary caregivers, staying home with children while the partner works outside the home. One father I knew was a stay-at-home, home-schooling parent. He said that he was far more nurturing and patient with the children than his wife, so when the children were older, they had decided he would stay home to care for them. In this situation, the mother was actually responsible for the playful interactions, and the dad was the nurturing parent.

Make sure that, as parents, you and your partner discuss the roles your parents played in your early lives and what roles you each want to play in your relationship with your own children. Do you have any discomfort with your perceived role in raising your children? Do you want to be more or less involved with your own children than your own parents were with you? What will your involvement look like from day to day, as you're raising your young children together?

The Importance of Male Role Models

In our society, for a variety of reasons, we have many absent fathers, or children who never have positive experiences with men while growing up. It is important to recognize that children need positive male role models—fathers, uncles, grandfathers, neighbors, teachers, family friends—in their lives. For boys, this positive male role model helps them to understand how to be a nurturing male. For girls, this positive male role model gives them the experience of what it means to be treated with respect by a man. For both boys and girls, these experiences have a powerful effect on the relationships they choose as they grow older, including the partners they select when they grow up. (See Harville Hendrix's book *Keeping the Love You Find* for a more in-depth discussion of how our early relationships influence our challenges as adults, particularly in our intimate relationships.)

Babies and the Stoplight States

When we invest time and energy in our family early on, focusing on creating connected, healthy relationships, we become very sensitive to the needs of our family members. When we start out on a connected, green-light state, we are more aware when circumstances begin to shift anyone into a less connected, yellow-light state, and barring unforeseen traumas, we can avoid ending up in a red-light state of total disconnection, where we are focusing only on survival. For a full summary of the stoplight states, please see Book I of the Consciously Parenting series, *Consciously Parenting: What It Really Takes to Raise Emotionally Healthy Families.*

The following chart lists specific behaviors or actions that can move families into each of the stoplight states when children are under the age of three.

Green Light	Yellow Light	Red Light
Educating ourselves about what babies need and how parents can best meet those needs Practicing conscious conception, pregnancy, and birth Following a connection-parenting philosophy Employing babywearing—using a sling to carry our babies close to our bodies during the day Leaving the car seat in the car and holding our babies as much as possible when they're not in the car	Putting all parental needs above the baby's needs Neglecting parental needs to care only for baby's needs; ignoring our feelings Seeing adult motives behind the baby's "negative" behaviors; assuming that babies can think like adults and act with the same motivations that adults do Using negative language to describe the baby or the baby's behaviors	Following without question or thought all common cultural practices regarding conception, pregnancy, and birth Letting the baby "cry it out" Ignoring a baby's cries when we think there is no reason for the baby to be crying Rigidly maintaining a daily feeding and/or sleeping schedule based solely on the parents' convenience Frequently separating the baby from the primary parent Limiting access to breastfeeding

(continued)

Green Light	Yellow Light	Red Light
Co-sleeping or sleeping in close proximity	Focusing on the baby's individual behaviors and how to make those behaviors stop	Not holding a bottle-feeding baby, but instead propping up the bottle so that a parent doesn't need to be close while the baby is feeding
Responding to the baby's nighttime needs		
Basing our daily and weekly schedule on the baby's natural sleeping and feeding patterns, rather than following a rigid schedule	Relying on folklore or second-hand information when making parenting decisions	Limiting physical touch or having no physical contact with the baby
	Focusing solely on the moment in front of us rather than parenting with the end goals in mind	Frequently leaving the baby in the crib or car seat (A flat head is one late sign that a baby is spending way too much time in the crib and/or car seat.)
Feeding (preferably breastfeeding) when the baby is hungry, rather than "clock" feeding		
Bottle nursing when breastfeeding not possible (and holding our baby in a breast-feeding position while they're drinking from the bottle)	Expecting that having a baby will not change our life; fitting the baby into our existing life rather than focusing on the baby's needs (convenience parenting)	Not treating a primary parent's depression
		Holding a negative outlook on parenting and the baby
Taking time for ourselves as needed		Giving a toddler time-outs (Focusing only on making a behavior go away creates a discon-nection in the relation-ship and doesn't allow for understanding of why the toddler is acting in this particular way.)
Taking care of our needs for self-care and community		

All of us probably experienced some of the yellow-light and red-light list items at one point or another in our childhoods. And perhaps we've also done some of these things as parents, because we thought it was what we were supposed to do, we weren't aware that we had other choices, or we were simply too overwhelmed to do anything else. The point of this list is not to make anyone feel bad, but help us become aware of which actions and behaviors create a healthy family relationship between parents and babies and which do not.

If you find that you're in a pattern of using many of the yellow- and red-light parenting behaviors, or if you were in the past, stop and breathe. Awareness is the first step of creating any sort of change in your life and in your family. As you continue reading, choose one area where you'd like to make changes that feel doable for you and your family. Remember, this is a process, not an event. Parenting is a long-term process of relationship and attunement, and each step you make toward creating connection counts.

Moving from Yellow Light to Red Light: The Window of Tolerance

In many of his academic lectures and academic papers, psychologist and UCLA professor Allan Schore talks about a window of tolerance and children's ability to deal with the stressors in their lives. That window is the amount of stress a person can handle; when the stress level exceeds our window of tolerance, we reach a point where we can take no more. We all have such a point, and when we were very small infants, some of us reached that point on a regular basis. Some young children can withstand quite a bit of the less-than-ideal parenting behaviors described in the yellow-light and red-light columns of the previous list, while others will shut down or move into a state of survival (fight, flight, or freeze mode) relatively quickly. According to my research, there are a wide range of factors that contribute to how much children can withstand, including early nutrition, genetics, epigenetics, and particularly the timing and severity of shocks to the baby's nervous system during pregnancy, birth, and the early postpartum period, along with the parent's own story and ability to cope with stress.

Are we putting our children in situations that exceed their ability to cope and, in doing so, teaching our children helplessness? Or are we teaching our children that they are important and that we will be there for them whenever possible? Part of the fine art of parenting is learning when our children need a nudge forward to develop and when something is pushing them too far outside of their comfort zone. By consciously creating a connected relationship with our children from the very beginning of their lives, we can start to learn what this balance looks like for each child and, thus, what he or she needs at a given moment.

As an example, Bill and Mary were the proud new parents of Benjamin, who, at three months old, was a very happy baby. Mary wore Benjamin in a sling throughout the day, keeping him close. Benjamin slept in a co-sleeper next to his parents' bed at night.

Then Bill and Mary were given a copy of a book that said Benjamin's "habit" of waking a few times during the night was the start of a very bad long-term habit that needed to be stopped right away, or they would regret it. They decided to follow the recommendations for sleep-training Benjamin. They moved him from the co-sleeper to a crib and began to let him cry when he woke up so that he would learn to go to sleep on his own. While Benjamin cried inside the crib, Mary cried outside his bedroom door. After a little over a week, the crying stopped, and Bill and Mary felt they had successfully broken Benjamin's "bad" sleeping habit.

But then a friend pointed out that something didn't seem right with Benjamin. He had been so happy before, and now he just seemed rather sad and depressed. She also asked why they weren't holding Benjamin in the sling anymore. Her questions prompted Bill and Mary to notice that Benjamin, their once very happy baby, didn't seem as happy anymore. And Mary realized that she had also started leaving him in his car seat, rather than holding him, for longer times.

Once Mary realized that she and Benjamin were disconnected from each other, she reversed everything: she returned Benjamin to his co-sleeper beside their bed at night and resumed holding him in the sling throughout the day. She told little Benjamin how sorry she was for leaving him like that, and they cried together. In a few short days, Benjamin was back to his old self.

How can we recognize the signs that our child is experiencing too much stress or trauma? How much is too much? There is no one, right answer. We usually don't know what our baby's window of tolerance is until he or she is completely overwhelmed. The best advice I can give is to limit the amount of yellow- and red-light parenting behaviors (some of which may be easier to avoid than others, depending upon your own early experiences) and increase the number of green-light behaviors. If you do notice that your baby has gone past what he or she can tolerate, return to more attachment-type experiences.

In the case of Mary, Bill, and Benjamin, a friend's observations alerted Mary and Bill to a change in their baby's behavior. If your baby becomes fussier and more clingy or, conversely, seems to suddenly become "too good," with a glazed over expression on his face, you have exceeded your child's window of tolerance. If your baby is calm and happy, connecting well, and able to snuggle in when upset, your baby is probably staying within his own window of tolerance.

Notice your own reactions, too, as connected parents often have a sense of what their baby needs. If, like Mary, you sob at the idea of leaving your baby alone and crying in her crib, you are in a yellow- or red-light state yourself and need to do whatever it takes to return yourself to a state in which you can connect with yourself and your baby. (Suggestion: go pick up your baby!)

How can we help our young children get back to and spend more time in a green-light state? We can proactively create connection in our relationships with them with any or all of the following:

- responding to our babies' communication

- minimizing the number of things we put between us and our babies

- babywearing—using a sling or soft carrier to carry our babies close to our bodies

- breastfeeding

- shared sleeping or co-sleeping

Reminder: Even when you are doing "everything right," your child still will have times when she needs to cry. Having a baby who is crying "for no apparent reason" doesn't mean that you're not doing a good job connecting. Part of parenting is realizing that babies, like adults, will have times when they're upset. And just like us, children need us to be with them when they cry, even if we don't understand why they're upset. When your child is having a hard day, remember that you have an opportunity to connect with him.

Let's look at how each of the above "tools" helps us connect to our babies and young children.

Responsiveness

Babies and young children need us to be responsive to their communications—especially their cries. We cannot teach our young children to not have needs. When we fail to respond to them, we only teach them to disconnect from their needs. Much of the currently available parenting information about young children suggests that we need to teach them to be more independent, even though research shows that young children become overwhelmed when they are not supported. They need us to help them learn how to regulate their emotional states and their behavior. By responding to our children's communication, we are creating connection with them.

However, responding to our child's communications, especially as they grow into toddlerhood, does not mean giving them whatever they want. If what they want is a basic need—touch, food (good food), sleep, affection, physical or emotional presence—we need to make every effort to meet those needs. If what they want is not a basic need, we need to ask ourselves whether, in this case, it would be best to set a limit (see guiding principle 7) or give our children what they desire.

Parents who struggle with balancing the needs and wants of young children fall into two categories, and which category they fall into is related to how they were raised. (Sometimes parents do the same things their own parents did; sometimes they do exactly the opposite of what their parents did.) Permissive parents let their children do whatever they want. Sometimes they do so in the name of meeting their children's needs and not thwarting their child's emerging independence, as well as wanting to keep their children from getting upset. Other parents micromanage their children and try to control every behavior. I knew one mother who did not allow her daughter to have any more than one toy at a time—and the girl had only just turned two. We need to find that balance between letting our children do whatever they want and allowing them freedom for exploration.

As a general rule, say yes as much as possible. Most of us have heard the word *no* far more times than *yes* by the time we are six years old. What does a world filled with *no* do to our creativity and exploration? It creates limits in our own lives when there need not be limits. However, if what your children want might threaten their safety or health, don't be afraid to set limits. (It isn't OK to play in the street. It isn't OK to eat foods they're allergic to or to eat ice cream every day for breakfast.)

Setting Limits, Respecting Feelings

Our children aren't always happy when we set a limit with them. This doesn't mean that we need to revoke our limit and stop the flood of feelings that might result from our child being unhappy.

If you feel strongly that it isn't acceptable for your child to eat ice cream for breakfast, you can still allow space for your child to be unhappy about the limit while still holding to the no ice cream before lunch rule. Remember that children often express their disappointments when we set a limit and often it isn't really about the limit we just set. It is the straw that broke the camel's back and feelings from many other disappointments come spilling out. We can create the space for our children to be upset, to connect with their disappointments, and to still hold to our limit.

When we need to set a limit, we can validate our child's feelings. "Yes, I know you really wanted to have ice cream for breakfast today and it is so disappointing when you can't have something you really want." This gives us an opportunity to connect with how our child is probably feeling and to mirror those feelings back to our child while naming them. (Dr. Daniel Seigel frequently talks about the importance of naming feelings- "name it to tame it.") When we can imagine situations in which we have been disappointed about something not going the way we wanted it to go, even

(continued)

if we can't understand our child's disappointment in this situation, we're creating empathy and connection with our child's world. So by setting the limit and respecting the feelings, we're creating an opportunity for more connection, even when we are saying no.

For more information on setting limits and respecting feelings, please see Chapter 8 of Book I, *Consciously Parenting: What it Really Takes to Raise Emotionally Healthy Families.*

During infancy, frequent, close physical contact with the parents is critical to babies' optimal development. Try using a sling during the day to keep your baby close, and co-sleep or sleep in close proximity to your baby at night. Leave the car seat in the car. Those car seats that attach to a stroller and have a carrying handle may seem convenient, but they don't take into account the fact that babies need to be held. Babies need to bond with a real person, to feel the skin of a real person, and to regulate their breathing by being in close proximity to their parents. Pull your baby out of the car seat and carry her with joy, knowing that doing so benefits both of you.

Follow your baby's cues for such activities as feeding, sleeping, and playing. So much parenting information goes into great detail about how children *should* eat at certain intervals or *should* sleep at certain times for certain lengths of time. Those suggestions pull you out of relationship with your child. Instead of paying attention to your child's cues and staying attuned to your child's needs, you are parenting by the clock. Children whose cues are ignored learn to ignore their own body signals. For example, instead of learning to know when they are hungry because they are fed when they communicate hunger, these children will disconnect from their bodily sensations or have no association between their own signals of hunger and eating. In a world where obesity is an issue, this connection is of critical importance.

Paying attention to your child's cues doesn't mean that if you feel your child's eating or sleeping patterns are really out of balance that you don't get support or make changes by getting to the root of the challenge. Instead, we need to remember that our child is communicating with us all the time. Being curious about what your child is communicating is a great first step when your inner guidance says that something isn't quite right.

During the first few months of your baby's life especially, minimize noise and overstimulation by keeping your baby's world small. Avoid the TV, loud music, bright lights, and strong smells, including fabric softeners and heavily scented detergents. Young children up to about the age of five or six have no ability to filter out information or noise from the environment, so we need to be aware of the environment we put them into. While the womb is said to be a noisy place (think the constant noise of a vacuum cleaner), when our children are born, their senses can be very sensitive. This is particularly true of children who have experienced a difficult transition into the world. Often times, we are excited to show off our new baby and eager to take her out into the world, but in the early months, babies need very little outside stimulation other than direct physical and emotional contact with a small circle of people, particularly their mothers. All your baby really needs is you. You, on the other hand, may need some connection with the outside world, and you should definitely not ignore your own needs. Just be aware of the places you take your young baby while you are doing so. (i.e. A noisy mall is probably not the best place to take a young baby.) When we do venture out into the world, having our babies in close physical proximity to us, particularly in a sling or other soft carrier, provides another layer of protection from the outside world. Slings and being in arms can help to shield babies from the lights, sounds, and strangers with dirty hands who want to touch them.

More You, Less Stuff

Everyone is out to sell stuff to new parents. Baby equipment is a huge market, as parents spend hundreds of millions of dollars every year on things for babies who cannot even walk or talk. The ads in parenting magazines make it sound like babies need a lot of things; however, we need to remember that those ads are trying to sell us *things*.

There are also warnings every year about the dangers of the "family bed" from such organizations as the Consumer Product Safety Commission. In 2009, *Consumer Reports* published an issue about where babies should sleep. The problem was, the issue's information was not based on science. Fear sells products. We think we are endangering our children if we don't buy them certain toys, or we are being neglectful in our role as parents if we don't have *Baby Einstein* videos available for our infants to watch or we aren't teaching our baby to read. We don't want our child to be developmentally behind because of something we didn't buy.

When I was expecting my first child, the facilitator of my childbirth class said something that I have never forgotten: "Your baby doesn't care about any baby gadgets. All that your baby needs is you. The most important thing you can give your baby is you." She made a short list of what baby actually needs beyond his parents. This list included a soft baby carrier, perhaps a nursing pillow, diapers (she suggested cloth because they're reusable and less expensive than disposable diapers*), clothing, a couple of blankets (we were in south Florida, where it was rarely cold), a car seat, a newborn baby hat, and Mama's breasts. Everything else is optional.

The reality is that being in close contact with humans— not which baby swing we put our baby in or the way the nursery is decorated—is what keeps our baby out of survival mode, where all his resources and energy are devoted to just making it through the day and the night. Babies who are not held, nurtured, talked to, and loved in someone's arms are the ones who will not thrive. This truth runs counter to the parenting advice and practices we see in our culture. Minimizing the baby stuff in favor of giving our baby lots of attention and contact generally isn't what the Joneses are doing with their baby, and we may feel as if we are doing something wrong if we aren't going out and being the perfect consumer of baby products. This type of parenting is outside the norm. But we need to reassess our priorities so that the needs of young children are met and those children can grow up to be healthy individuals who are capable of nurturing their own children.

Delay buying lots of things your baby really doesn't need, and sit with your feelings about these ideas. How do you feel about having your baby need you and only you? This idea can be very scary for some parents, especially if we were raised in an environment where our parents had difficulty connecting with us and being there for us. Respect those feelings. They are a communication from your own past and will help you better understand yourself, which is the first step to being a conscious parent.

*See resources section for more information about cloth diapers.

Brain Development 101: Infants

In infancy, children are survival-brain dominant.

- Their behaviors are primarily reflexive and imitative.

(continued)

- The fight, flight, or freeze response is their dominant reaction to stress, and they do not have the ability to calm their own stress.

- They have no ability to regulate their own behavior and emotional states. When overwhelmed, they are simply thrown into survival mode, and when they are overwhelmed on a regular basis, they eventually learn to shut down (because they can't run away or fight).

- They learn primarily through the senses: touch, taste, sight, smell, hearing different sounds and tones of voice.

- The parts of their brains responsible for conscious remembering are not yet not developed. But what happens to them is stored in their bodies, and they will show their stories through their behaviors.

Tools for creating relationships with infants, based on brain development: Touch, soothing sounds, soft colors, human faces in close proximity, babywearing, co-sleeping, breastfeeding.

Avoid: Leaving babies alone when they are upset. (Children learn how to calm themselves through interaction with others, not through being left alone.) They have little ability to regulate their own behavior and emotional states.

Babywearing

You've probably seen those parents who use a sling or soft baby carrier to carry their children. Once these carriers were a rare sight, but it is now common to see at least some parents carrying their babies in a carrier rather than using a stroller or a car seat.

Children need connection with our bodies. They spent nine months in the womb in nearly constant motion, and they need that same intimate connection with us after they are born. Children are sensory creatures and need to smell us, touch us, hear us, see us, and taste us; they need the experience of us. A baby who is in isolation doesn't learn at the same rate as children who are carried in their parents' arms. Children who are by themselves a great deal and out of their parents' arms are more likely to be in survival mode, where all their resources and energy go into just staying alive. Remember that infants do not have the ability to understand where you have gone, why you are gone, or that you are coming back. We need to be physically present with our babies as much as possible, and using a sling makes it easy to keep our babies in close physical contact with us.

Slings have been fashioned from pieces of cloth for nearly as long as there have been mothers and babies. It is only recently that we've figured out how to fashion plastic car seats or other holding devices to put our babies in. Parents used to *have* to carry their babies to keep their infants out of harm's way while the parents completed necessary survival tasks requiring two hands, such as fetching water or harvesting food. The babies' safety needs were met, along with their emotional and physical needs for closeness, and the work got done. It was a great system! However, once we became more efficient with other tasks involved in living, and safety was no longer such an issue, we began focusing on how to put our babies down and get them to be happy about it. We lost some of the benefits that carrying our babies gives them (and us). Fortunately, this lost art of carrying babies close to our bodies has once again been discovered by savvy parents.

There are nearly as many slings available now as there are parents and babies who use them, so be ready to do a little research before you commit to one sling or another. Finding somewhere to "try before you buy" would be ideal. Do a Google search for sling reviews, and see which slings parents like the most or why they don't like a particular sling. Look for one that supports the baby, is adjustable, and is comfortable to wear (because of even weight distribution). A comfortable parent means a comfortable baby!

Once I found a sling that I liked and got used to using it, I was able to wear it while doing all sorts of tasks and still have both of my hands free. My baby was able to be in constant motion with me and to be a part of my life, rather than feeling like an inconvenience. His naps happened in my arms or in the sling, so I didn't need to plan my day according to his nap schedule when he was very little. He became very flexible about where and when he slept because he was attached to a person rather than a specific set of external physical circumstances, such as a specific crib or a "soothie" (anything children use to soothe themselves, such as blankets, stuffed toys, or pacifiers) to help him fall asleep on his own.

Slings can be used until children are around the age of three and sometimes beyond, depending on your child's size, the style of carrier you're using, and your ability to carry your child. Honestly, carrying your child in a sling is really good weight-bearing exercise. If you start carrying your baby when she is small, your body adjusts as she grows, and carrying her isn't a big deal even when she gets bigger. Dads can carry infants and toddlers around, too, and I encourage dads to do so. My husband was always very excited about being able to carry our children around in the sling, and he did attract some attention when he did it. Picture a large man—six feet, two inches tall—carrying a toddler in a brightly colored, patterned, purple cloth sling with large silver rings (a Maya wrap), and you might be able to under-stand why he turned heads! He actually started selling slings because so many people asked him where he bought the one he used.

Not all parents are able to carry their babies in slings. Some babies are very large and gain weight very quickly, while their parents have small frames. Other parents have back problems and have been cautioned not to lift too much weight on a regular basis. If at all possible, have at least one person who can wear the baby to give her the experience of being held and supported. If this is not possible, make sure that you make time for sitting and holding your baby as much as you can. It may feel like you're "doing nothing" or that your time could be better spent sweeping the floor, doing the dishes, or washing all that extra baby laundry that seems to come out of nowhere, but there is no greater investment than the time you spend with your infant. As your child grows bigger, the time spent holding and rocking him will become less and less frequent, yet for the rest of his life, your child will continue to reap the benefits of the time spent holding him while he was young. This experience will be stored in the cells of his body forever. Babies and young children who spent time being in arms are more likely to continue seeking our reassuring touch as they grow older, and being held is truly a need we never outgrow.

Babywearing is even more important when we have children who were born prematurely or who experienced birth trauma or medical trauma after birth. Being held next to a calm, regulated person's body helps them learn to calm their nervous systems and regulate their body systems.

Kangaroo care can be especially beneficial for premature babies. Kangaroo care basically recreates the womb environment for the fourth trimester (the first three to four months after a baby is born) and involves as much skin-to-skin contact as possible. It helps premature babies normalize their body temperature, heart rate, and breathing. Kangaroo care was discovered in a South American hospital that was lacking modern equipment to save a premature baby. The hospital staff decided that there was nothing else that could be done for the child, so they allowed the parents to hold their baby. A miraculous thing happened: the baby's heart rate normalized. The doctors continued to allow the parents to hold their child and were surprised when the baby was able to go home just a few weeks later. For more on kangaroo care, see *Kangaroo Care*, a great book published by La Leche League International.

Breastfeeding

Breastfeeding provides everything a baby needs in the early months of life: holding, food, and love. (Well, everything except diapers.)

When I was pregnant with my first child, I wasn't planning to breastfeed, and I was annoyed when I read that breastfeeding was a requirement for moms delivering at the birth center I'd chosen. No one was going to tell me what to do! The thought of breastfeeding, particularly in public, made me cringe. I wasn't sure I wanted to do it. And wasn't formula nearly the same as breast milk anyway? I had been a nanny for two infants—one who was completely formula fed and one whose mother tried to use breast milk exclusively and rarely resort to formula. Honestly, with the second mother, I didn't understand what the big fuss was about, but she had a clear disdain for the powdered substance.

Once again, it was my midwife, Debbie Marin, who educated me about the importance of breastfeeding and handed me a book called *The Womanly Art of Breastfeeding* published by La Leche League, an organization I had never heard of before. I was slightly embarrassed by the book's title, but I picked it up and began to read anyway. I started to understand that breastfeeding was about more than just a way of feeding a baby; it was about relationship. My early training about attachment kicked in, and I understood how this feeding choice could make a big difference in connecting with my baby. I also began to understand that breast milk was not the same as formula. The more I read, the more determined I became to breastfeed my baby and not give him any formula.

When formula samples arrived in the mail, I put them by the front door so that we could get them out of the house and donate them, as suggested in *The Womanly Art of Breastfeeding*. When my father-in-law came over and asked curiously why the samples were by the door, I told him my plan to get rid of the formula. He let me know that I should be cautious about giving the samples away because sometimes breastfeeding just doesn't work out. I interpreted that as a challenge and decided at that moment that I wasn't going to use it no matter what. Interestingly enough, that fortitude, along with the support of my husband, was just what I needed to make it through those most difficult early days of breastfeeding.

We ended up having many challenges, because even though breastfeeding is a very natural thing, it is something both mother and baby have to learn together. Some mother-baby pairs have an easier time learning than others. It is important to note that when the pregnancy is stressful or other overwhelming events happen during the birth or shortly after, breastfeeding challenges are more likely. Ray Castellino and Mary Jackson of About Connections suggest that babies show their stories when going to the breast. So if all other positioning and physical issues (such as inverted nipples) have been addressed and you're still experiencing challenges, it may be wise to consider that your baby is trying to communicate. When we can create the space to observe and listen to our baby, we may find that breastfeeding goes more smoothly. (For more information on Ray and Mary's work, see the "Little People, Big Challenges" programs available at www.consciouslyparenting.com/LPBC.) My baby and I eventually did get it all figured out and went on to a beautiful breastfeeding relationship.

A Good Start to Breastfeeding

Sometimes even the most prepared mothers can have difficulty breastfeeding. Below are some tips to help you get off to the best start possible.

Have the most natural birth possible.
When babies are born with medications in their systems, they are less able to coordinate sucking, swallowing, and breathing to breastfeed. And the more trauma a baby experiences during birth, the more likely a baby will have difficulty breastfeeding.

Strive to have the first feeding at the breast within 30 minutes of birth, when possible.
As long as mother and baby are healthy, everything else can wait. This includes the first bath, weighing and measuring and the newborn exam.

Avoid water or formula, bottles and pacifiers.
Newborns need only breast milk. Only in rare cases do babies need anything other than breast milk. Even if a baby is unable to nurse at the breast, the best food possible for a baby (and especially if the baby has health issues) is breast milk. It can be fed to the baby using a flexible cup or spoon.

Keep the mother-baby unit together after birth.
The more mom and baby are together, the more a baby will nurse. Breast milk is produced in a supply and demand relationship, so the more a baby nurses, the more milk the mother will produce.

If something traumatic happens during the birth, create space for yourself to tell your story and your baby to show his story. Breastfeeding is more likely to go well when supported through creating opportunities to integrate what happened.

Why Breastfeed? Does it Really Matter?

Breastfeeding is about so much more than food. It offers both short- and long-term physical and emotional benefits for babies, as well as for mothers.

No manmade product even comes close to the living, magical substance that is breast milk. The more that is learned about breast milk, the more amazing its apparent superpowers become.

First of all, breast milk changes according to the needs of the baby in that moment. How's that for attunement? If the baby is exposed to an illness, Mom's body responds by creating antibodies for that specific illness, and the baby takes in those antibodies through the breast milk. Breastfeeding can also help to prevent sudden infant death syndrome (SIDS). A meta-analysis—a study of all the studies ever done on a subject—published in the July 2011 issue of *Pediatrics Journal* irrefutably showed not only that breastfeeding has an impact on SIDS, but also that the more exclusively a baby is breastfed (meaning the baby receives no artificial baby milk), the more protection he or she receives.
(pediatrics.aappublications.org/content/128/1/103.abstract)

The consistency of breast milk changes during an individual feeding: The milk that comes out first is called foremilk and quenches the baby's thirst. The milk that comes out later in the feeding, called hindmilk, is fat rich and fills the baby's tummy. Breast milk consistency also changes from feeding to feeding during a single day. If the baby has nursed recently and is just needing to be in contact with Mom (a behavior called comfort nursing), the baby can make less milk come out of the breast. If the baby is growing, the mother's body will step up milk production to meet the baby's needs. Finally, the flavor of breast milk changes according to what the mother eats, exposing the baby to a wide variety of tastes common in the mother's culture and, in doing so, easing the child's later transition to table foods.

Breast milk customizes itself to the baby's changing needs because the mom's body is in constant communication with the baby's body. This intimate communication system also allows the baby to learn what her body needs and to learn that her needs are important and deserve to be respected. The system works perfectly—as long as parents do not interfere with it (by using "clock" feeding or a strict feeding schedule, for example). When babies' feeding cues are not respected, they disconnect from their own bodies. Later in their life, this disconnection can result in many food issues; they may overeat because they don't recognize their body's cues telling them that it is full, or they may undereat because they don't recognize when their body is telling them that it needs to be fed.

In contrast to breast milk, formula is always exactly the same. It is not a living substance and cannot change according to the needs of the baby. The World Health Organization (WHO) lists formula as the fourth and last choice of food for babies—not the second choice, as formula companies would have new parents believe. The first choice is breast milk directly from the mother's breast. Second best is expressed breast milk from the mother. Third is expressed breast milk from another woman. Fourth, and last, is formula. Formula is lifeless and static, and feeding it to infants is not the best way to grow a healthy baby.

The connections between breastfeeding and the risk of infant death are well documented, and it is well known in the breastfeeding community that not being breastfed is a huge risk factor for infant death. Each year, hundreds of thousands of infant deaths around the world—thousands in the United States alone—can be directly attributed to babies not being breastfed. Breastfeeding lowers the risk of infant death in general and specifically lowers the risk of SIDS.

Infant deaths that could have been prevented with breastfeeding are not limited to third-world countries. I had two cousins in the United States who nearly died because they could not digest the formula their mother, my aunt, gave them instead of breast milk. We Americans tend to think that we are immune from such infant-mortality problems because we are such a modern society, but babies simply were not designed to grow optimally while eating a manmade substance.

Breastfeeding is often made to seem like an inconvenience compared to formula, especially in the first few weeks of a baby's life. After all, the breastfeeding baby seems to wake often, and only Mom can feed the baby. But ask any bottle-feeding parent how convenient it is to carry bottles and formula when leaving the house, or to get up in the middle of the night to fix a bottle. During natural disasters, such as Hurricane Katrina in New Orleans, mothers who were breastfeeding their babies always had a supply of food for the babies because they did not need clean water and clean bottles, which are needed to make formula. Breast milk is always the right temperature, always readily available, comes in attractive containers, and constantly changes to meet the needs of a growing baby.

Breastfeeding's benefits don't end with the nutritional benefits of breast milk. Breastfeeding actually helps babies to attach to their parents, as well as helping their parents to bond with them. We now know from James McKenna, an infant-mother sleep researcher with the University of Notre Dame, and the studies he has done at his Mother-Baby Behavioral Sleep Laboratory (cosleeping.nd.edu) that infants are designed to wake frequently at night to nurse and connect with their parents. This biological and physiological connection is part of what lowers the risk of SIDS for babies sleeping in close proximity to parents at night, which often happens when babies are breastfeeding. The hormones released in a breastfeeding mother's milk actually boost bonding by giving Mom a strong desire to be with her baby. (This hormonal boost of breastfeeding can be especially important for moms who did not have strong early relationships with their own parents and, as a result, need some biological help to start connecting with their own babies.)

Also, the longest distance a baby can see clearly at birth is twelve to eighteen inches—exactly the distance between a mother's eyes and the baby at her breast. The eye contact that happens between a mother and baby during breastfeeding, in combination with the sweet taste of breast milk, activates the part of the brain that is responsible for attachment. Attachment is a relationship that necessarily includes two people: one person responsible for bonding (the parent, who creates an environment where there is space to connect) and one responsible for attaching in response to the bonding (the baby). It's a two-way street.

Finally, breastfeeding promotes proper mouth and jaw development. Dentist Brian Palmer's website has extensive information about how a baby's facial bones, jaw, and airways are actually molded from being positioned correctly at the breast. Palmer said that he could look into the mouth of an adult and tell whether or not the person was breastfed as an infant!

Truly, we are just beginning to understand the enormous impact breastfeeding (or not breastfeeding) has on our health for our lifetime.

Obstacles to Breastfeeding

Even when we're convinced that breastfeeding is worth pursuing with our new baby, we may find that the path isn't paved with gold. Unfortunately, sometimes even health-care providers become obstacles to successful breastfeeding. Some pediatricians are wonderful. The one I saw when my oldest son was a baby was very knowledgeable about breastfeeding and breastfed-baby norms. But when I became a La Leche League leader, I started hearing from many parents who did not have that same professional support. Some of these moms received poor information, which led to milk-supply difficulties or babies who wouldn't latch onto the breast.

Sometimes our pediatricians simply don't have the information to support breastfeeding and the breastfeeding relationship. Many pediatricians know that "breast is best," but get their information from formula-company representatives who are trying to sell their product and make money when a family decides to use formula. Old, outdated, and inaccurate information based upon the assumption that formula is always safer than breast milk (information from back in the days when formula was the "modern" thing to use) is still in circulation, and many doctors still base their recommendations on it.

If your chosen health-care professionals can't give you the support or information you need, keep looking for someone who can. Do your own research, and consult with an internationally board certified lactation consultant (IBCLC) if you have any doubts. La Leche League is also a good source of information about current breastfeeding issues. La Leche League leaders are specially trained mothers who can answer questions and provide support free of charge. And keep in mind that there are very few situations where breastfeeding isn't an option.

Even when mothers have a strong desire to breastfeed, sometimes they reach a point where the difficulties seem insurmountable. Maybe the baby is nursing all the time and never seems satisfied. Perhaps the baby is waking frequently to nurse. Maybe the baby's weight gain is slow, or the baby is pulling at the breast and hurting the mother physically. These are situations where compassion and support are needed. Many mothers quit at this point, while other mothers push on even though it is not working.

If breastfeeding is difficult, there is a reason. Remember, babies show their stories on the journey to the breast. When the story is recognized, these kinds of challenges often go away.

I once received a phone call from a father with a three-day-old baby who was chomping at the mother's breast while trying to feed. This mother was 100 percent committed to breastfeeding—she had been imagining breastfeeding her own child since she was a little girl—but her daughter's breastfeeding behaviors had her in tears and ready to quit. Honestly, I wouldn't have blamed her if she had quit at that point. When I started asking about the baby's birth, the father told me that the baby was born in a birth center with a midwife and there had been no interventions. Then I asked if someone had suctioned the baby after birth. From the background, I heard Mom yell, "Yes! They did. It was horrible."

I went to see the family to help them recover from this overwhelming event, and I was curious to see if the chomping would stop when we addressed the story of the birth. Little Ariel lay on her mother's stomach and slept, while Mom and Dad, though exhausted, supported one another as they told their story. When they finished, Ariel helpfully woke up and began moving toward her mother's breast. I predicted that she would get very fussy when she got there, because she would be showing the part of her birth story when someone pushed something down her throat (the suctioning). And I was right—she reached the breast and began wailing. I encouraged both parents to talk to her about what had happened, to tell Ariel her story. Soon everyone was crying along with the baby. And after a few minutes, the baby latched onto the mother's breast and nursed without chomping for several minutes—the first time she'd ever done so.

Ariel's parents continued talking to her prior to feeding—either nursing or bottle feeding—and within two days, Ariel was nursing happily. Plus, she and Mom were connected to each other. I think a big part of this story is that Mom and Baby both understood what was being communicated. It wasn't just the telling of a story, but the emotional connection that happened when the story was told. Ariel wasn't trying to hurt her mother, and Mom hadn't done anything wrong. But once Mom understood that Ariel needed more support specifically when attaching at the breast, there was a softening, and the relationship blossomed. Last I heard, the entire family was doing very well.

For more information on how to use story sharing to support your family after overwhelming events, please check out the audio and transcript of a conversation I had on this topic with Ray Castellino and Mary Jackson of About Connections. (www.consciouslyparenting.com/LPBC)

There are cases in which a mother decides not to breast-feed, or she weans prematurely and then decides to breastfeed later after the milk has dried up or decreased substantially. Some women choose to relactate (start nursing again if their milk supply has stopped or dried up) or induce lactation (start making milk) with the support of herbs or medications, so they can partially or completely breastfeed. Some women are even able to induce lactation in order to breastfeed their adopted babies.

If you wanted to breastfeed, but weren't able to because of an overwhelming situation with your baby, understand that you can still connect with your baby (or even an older child) and share your disappointment at not being able to nurse. Also, when you're mindful of the benefits of breastfeeding, you can create opportunities to connect in ways that are naturally part of the breastfeeding relationship.

What's so Special about Breastfeeding Anyway?

Essential needs of infants for optimal development:

- Holding
- Feeding
- Love

Breastfeeding meets all three needs.

Tips if you Can't (or Didn't) Breastfeed

Breastfeeding isn't possible in every parenting circumstance. Perhaps you adopted your child, or you have other medical issues that prevent or hinder breastfeeding. Let's look at ways some parents in these circumstances have connected with their children as much as possible when feeding them.

There are ways to help your baby get the benefits of breastfeeding, including skin-to-skin contact and time at the breast in your arms, even if you aren't producing a full milk supply. Some women use a supplemental nursing system, a bottle-and-tube device that connects supplemental milk to the mother's nipple. When the baby latches onto the breast, a small tube delivers the milk (pumped breast milk, donated breast milk, or formula).

Another option is bottle nursing, a bottle-feeding method in which the behaviors of breastfeeding are mimicked as closely as possible. Bottle nursing involves holding the baby in a cradle position, skin-to-skin; looking into the baby's eyes; tickling the baby's lips with the bottle nipple; and waiting until the baby opens her mouth. Instead of feeding until the bottle is empty, you follow your baby's cues to know when he's ready to eat and watch him for signs that he has had enough to eat.

For children who weren't breastfed or who didn't have their need met to be lovingly held during feedings, you can offer them a bottle even if they are much older than infants. Those older children who still need this loving physical closeness will take the bottle. I suggest adding a little vanilla and slightly sweetening the milk (I like natural sweeteners like Stevia or Just Like Sugar, which has a low glycemic index) to mimic the sweetness of breast milk. Then you would hold your child in your arms and look lovingly into her eyes (if she'll let you). Bottle nursing an older child is a wonderful bonding experience if your child missed this close type of feeding earlier in her life, if weaning happened before she was ready, or if you weren't there for her to bond with (such as when children are adopted). Those who don't need this type of connection won't let you give them a bottle, and those who do accept it will let you know when they don't need it anymore. But to have their needs fully met, most children need this kind of connection with us much longer than most baby books indicate.

Breastfeeding and the Importance of Dad (and Other Nonbreastfeeding Caregivers)

Many fathers are confused about the father's role with a breast-fed baby. Some dads feel as if they can't do anything if they can't feed the baby, but nothing could be further from the truth. Dads (and moms' other parenting partners) can have a tremendous impact on the mother-baby breastfeeding relationship.

To be successful at breastfeeding, a mom needs the support of her parenting partner, especially in the early days and weeks of the breastfeeding relationship. During my early, challenging weeks of breastfeeding my first baby, I wouldn't have continued to breastfeed if it hadn't been for the support of my husband. He was there in the middle of the night to encourage me. He drove me to Miami, more than an hour away from our home, to visit the lactation consultant, Faith Ploude, who helped my son and me get back on track with breastfeeding.

About eight years ago, I met a mom who did not have the support of her husband. Breastfeeding was going well, the baby was thriving, but Dad wanted it to stop. He felt that his wife and his child were too connected. In hindsight, I think perhaps he was jealous of the baby being so close to his wife when his own early needs had not been met. The mom was bottle-feeding in front of her husband and secretly nursing when he wasn't home, until her milk finally dried up when the baby was about three months old. I was incredibly sad for this family—for the mother who wanted to breastfeed, for the father who hadn't had his own needs met, and for the baby who would no longer enjoy the closeness that was so essential for optimal development.

In addition to supporting Mom, partners can educate themselves about why breastfeeding is important for the health of babies. This information will come in handy if Mom encounters bumps in the breastfeeding road during the early days. As a La Leche League leader, I have received many calls from dads who are concerned about how breastfeeding is going or who are reaching out for support because Mom is simply too overwhelmed to pick up the phone. (I loved to hear from those dads!)

The parenting partner can also change diapers, bathe the baby, read to the baby, carry the baby in a sling, and be part of the nighttime routine. Sometimes we need to get creative to find nonfeeding aspects of baby care that create connection and support the role of the mother in the early days of infancy. One father loved to spend skin-to-skin time with his newborn son, letting the baby lie on his bare chest and sleep between feedings. Another father carried his daughter in a sling while he was doing some household tasks so that her mom could rest between feedings. Think outside the box, and you'll find a way to connect with your own baby and support your partner at the same time.

Incidentally, studies have shown that even fathers and other caregivers can begin producing mothering hormones (and also experience a drop in testosterone) when caring for babies. While the hormonal shifts experienced by other caregivers aren't nearly as strong as those experienced by breastfeeding mothers, caring for babies in a nurturing way increases the bond in the relationship on every level.

Breastfeeding: Not Just for Infants Anymore

In recent years, we have been given lots of information saying that breastfeeding a baby for longer than about six months means Mom has some sort of pathology or unmet needs. As a mother who has breastfed two babies for much longer than six months (think years), I can attest that breastfeeding a baby into toddlerhood is not about the mother's needs. Anthropological research suggests that humans are meant to be breastfed much longer than the typical one year recommended by the American Academy of Pediatrics, which has adjusted its statement to add:

"Or as long after [the age of] one as is mutually agreeable." The World Health Organization recommends a minimum of two years of breastfeeding.

Have you heard of milk teeth, the first set of teeth babies have? The fact that children don't lose their milk teeth until they are around six years old suggests that breast milk is meant to be part of their diet for several years past infancy. Sociological research suggests a similar time frame for weaning. After looking at many factors, including the amount of time it takes for the brain in different animals to mature, the average ages of weaning in other animals, and the average weaning ages in primitive societies, sociologists now think humans are intended to wean between the ages of two and a half and six years.

"What?!" you may be saying. "I didn't make it past the first few months!" or "I couldn't make it to one year!" or simply, "Are you crazy?"

Breastfeeding into toddlerhood and beyond is a wonderful parenting strategy that many parents miss out on entirely. When a child is upset, the child comes to the parent to nurse and connect. The breastfeeding mother releases hormones that create connection and relaxation within herself, which helps promote bonding. Breastfeeding when they are upset helps children create a means of calming down after something stressful happens, and they learn to go to a person for comfort, rather than later relying on things (such as drugs, alcohol, or food) to soothe their stress. Those patterns begin early. Honestly, I'm not sure I would have made it through the toddler years if I hadn't breastfed my first child and had breastfeeding in my parenting toolbox!

An important note about breastfeeding and comfort nursing: Breastfeeding can certainly be a wonderful way to help soothe a tired child to sleep and can be effective for connecting with a child at certain times of the day. However, some parents use nursing in a way that doesn't give the child space to express his feelings. When the baby or young child begins to express something, the mother automatically puts the child to the breast, and he is silenced. If children are nursed every time they are upset and don't learn how to move through their feelings, these children can have a very hard time when they are older and no longer nursing.

One mother came into my office with her three-month-old daughter, Selena, who was often pulling at her breast when Mom would try to nurse her. As I watched, I could see that Selena was trying to express something and didn't want to nurse. Mom wasn't intending to silence her; she just wanted Selena to calm. When the mother created the space for Selena to have her feelings, the baby was able to nurse without pulling at the breast at all.

Sometimes parents who are overwhelmed by their baby's expression of feelings feel the need to soothe the baby all the time so that they aren't overwhelmed. If this is the case for you, seek support from someone who can be there for you as your baby expresses his or her feelings.

Shared Sleep (Bed-Sharing) and Co-sleeping (Separate Surface)

Another parenting tool that complements breastfeeding is sleeping in close proximity to the baby at night. This can be through co-sleeping, which has the baby and parents sleeping near each other, but on separate surfaces, or through bed-sharing. Sleeping in close proximity helps to facilitate the breast-feeding relationship and the connection between mother and baby during the night. And connection (or disconnection) at night has a way of affecting the whole relationship.

For most of time, babies and their parents have slept close to one another. In most primitive societies around the world, babies and young children still sleep near the parents. Only in the past century or so, and only in developed societies, have babies started having their own rooms away from the parents. I'm not saying that you need to get a mat and sleep on the floor next to your baby's crib, but research has found that when Mom sleeps near the baby, the arrangement benefits them both in many ways.

James McKenna's sleep research has shown that the sleep cycles of co-sleeping mothers and babies synchronize in a way that doesn't happen with solitary-sleeping infants. Babies are actually meant to be in a lighter phase of sleep than adults. Those babies who go into a deep sleep state are those who are sleeping alone. And these solitary-sleeping babies are more likely to forget to breathe than those who stay in a lighter state of sleep and wake more frequently. McKenna's research shows that solitary-sleeping infants are at a greater risk for SIDS because they go into a very deep sleep that is biologically not appropriate. This is why the American Academy of Pediatrics has recommended that infants sleep in the same room as the parent caring for them, until they are at least six months old.

When they are co-sleeping, moms won't be awoken from a deep sleep, as happens when their baby is sleeping in another room, because they naturally move into a lighter sleep phase with their baby. When my oldest child was a baby, I often found that I would naturally wake up a few minutes before he would in the middle of the night. At first I wondered why I was awake when my baby was still sleeping, but when this cycle happened several times, I finally began to understand that we were connected somehow. How cool is that?

Regardless of whether the baby is sleeping in your bed or close to it, you do need to make sure you create a safe place for your baby. If you are co-sleeping on separate surfaces, pull the baby's crib close to your own bed and eliminate any gaps between the two. Some parents take off one side of the crib and join the crib to their adult bed for more space. Others put several mattresses on the floor and create a giant, bed-filled room.

Typical strategies to alter babies' natural sleeping behavior need to be examined critically, particularly the cry-it-out method of getting your baby to "learn" to sleep through the night.

Waking at night is biologically normal for babies because breast milk, the optimal food for babies, is digested quickly; therefore, babies need to be fed breast milk frequently. However, if your baby is waking very often and your internal alarms are going off and you feel that something isn't right, listen to yourself and find a way to support your baby in a gentle way. Consider checking out the "Little People, Big Challenges" audio program on sleep challenges for more information about helping your child to change sleep patterns without resorting to methods that don't respect the baby's communication.

Helping Children Transition to Solo Sleeping

Our need for physical closeness and connection does not stop once we turn one year old. Look at the sleeping arrangements of many cohabitating adults: we tend to sleep with our partners. Yet we expect young children to sleep alone and get their needs for comfort met by objects (pacifiers, blankets, and dolls) instead of people.

Most sleep information talks about the no-nos of sleep, and co-sleeping or sharing sleep is usually at the top of the no-no list. It is referred to as a bad habit that is best avoided in the first place. The parenting advice goes on to suggest that if you do find yourself co-sleeping with your child, it is best to go cold turkey and put your child into her own bed immediately. Strategies recommended by some pediatricians and other "sleep specialists" include locking a child's bedroom door so that a child cannot get out of her room at night. (Remember our definition of trauma: an overwhelming event in which the fight, flight, or freeze response is activated. Does being locked in a room, unable to get out, sound like that type of event to you?)

Children who share sleep space with their parents will eventually be ready to move to their own space, in their own time. Some children are ready early—between the ages of two and a half and three years. It is about this time when children develop the ability to understand that you don't disappear at night. Also about this time, children who have had their early need for responsive care met develop the ability to soothe their own distress (due to the development of the hippocampus, which helps soothe the activation of the amygdala in the brain). Other children may stick around in their parents' room past the age of three. These children often have a greater need for physical comfort and connection than others their age. This is especially true when their parents are away during the day and their comfort and connection needs are met only at night. Some parents find that when they increase the time they are fully emotionally present with their children during the day, their children's need to be close at night subsides.

When they are ready for their own space, some toddlers spontaneously leave the family bed, as it is often called, and move to a bed in their own room. Other toddlers first move on to a mattress on the floor of their parents' room as a transition to sleeping in their own room. Some children move out of their parents' room to sleep with an older sibling.

When helping your child transition to sleeping on her own, go at *her* pace, whatever that looks like. Introduce the idea that she will soon be ready to sleep in her own bed and in her own room, and give her time to get used to this idea. Perhaps talk about another child who is older, maybe a sibling or a friend, and sleeping in his own bed. If you have been sharing sleep with your child in the same bed, perhaps begin by setting up a special bed of her own in your room. When she's ready (and you can know this only by watching her), you can prompt her to move to the other bed, or, if you have some time to wait, your child will move there on her own. When that sleeping arrangement is comfortable for everyone, introduce the idea that her bed will move into her own room or space. For some children, this process will take only a night or two. For others, it may take months.

If a sleep strategy doesn't feel right to you, don't do it. If it is traumatic, don't do it. If a recommended strategy isn't gradual and respectful of your child's needs, it isn't in your child's best interest or in the best interest of your relationship in the long term. And if you need additional support to lovingly transition your child, the phone consultants at the Consciously Parenting Project can help. Sometimes additional issues may be at play, and additional support might be needed to make the transition.

Regardless of where your child is, stay open to the idea that children have nighttime needs, and that the idea of sleeping alone is a product of culture and financial gain for those who make devices that separate parents and children.

Most importantly, stay aware of your own feelings. Don't let a child stay in your bed if you resent the child's need to be close. Take a look at what needs weren't met for you when you were young, or what needs are not being met for you in the current sleeping arrangement. Talk about your feelings with someone who can really hear you, or spend some time writing about them. Where do your feelings come from? I suggest that your feelings are probably not just about your child. Were your early needs for physical contact met? If not, what can you do to meet this need now? If you have a partner, would he or she be willing to hold you? Do you resent your child for taking away your time with your partner? Finding a strategy that will meet everyone's needs is part of being a parent.

Meeting Your Own Needs

Creating healthy relationships with our children doesn't mean that we don't take care of our own needs. It means that we have to meet our needs without disregarding those of our

(continued)

young child, who can't understand that we are just going on vacation and will be back in a few days.

As guiding principle 8 of consciously parenting says, we need a community of people who can help us to raise our young children. Bruce Perry, author of *The Boy Who Was Raised as a Dog*, is a psychiatrist and brain researcher specializing in children who have experienced trauma. In a private lecture, he made a comment that a child under the age of six needs approximately four emotionally mature adult caregivers if he or she is to grow into a healthy, well-adjusted adult. For most of time, we have lived in small communities where these ratios have been the norm. Now, however, we are all living in our own separate houses without much community, trying to meet the needs of our children with a child-adult ratio that is typically at least two children to one adult for most of the day.

Our children need us to be present and emotionally mature. When we're completely exhausted from trying to run the house and meet all of our children's needs, plus working outside the home, we cannot adequately meet anyone's needs. As a friend reminded me, you can't give someone a dollar if you have only a nickel.

Creating healthy relationships means that we create support networks for ourselves. Those networks can include local relatives who support our type of parenting or other kindred spirits who are open to helping out. When we start looking around our community, we may suddenly find many opportunities to connect with others who are willing and happy to play a role in the lives of our children. It really does take a village—an intentional, conscious village—to raise a child. And by making the effort to find others to create and share that village with us, we can change the world, one child and one family at a time.

Chapter Three

Creating Connection Between Ages Three and Five

Beyond the age of three, children still have the same basic needs—touch, food (good food), sleep, affection, the physical and emotional presence of their caregivers—and meeting those needs will help you continue to build your relationship with your young child. As children grow, they present new opportunities for us to flex our parenting muscles. They're smarter, quicker, funnier, more curious, and sometimes much more trouble than they were from birth to age three, and their development requires us to get smarter to stay connected with them. Following are specific tips for continuing to build a relationship, founded on respect and love, with your children between the ages of three and five.

Respect your child's readiness for separation— and your own readiness. Between the ages of three and five, many children have their first experience of being cared for by a nonrelative. Many children also start some form of schooling at this time. Children who are securely attached may readily separate, knowing that they are safe with another person, or they may protest being separated from their parents. Both reactions are normal. Some children are ready to separate from their parents earlier than others.

Separation is especially an issue when we add preschool into the lives of our children. Preschool can be a wonderful experience for our little explorers, but it can also bring its own set of challenges. The pressure many parents feel to leave their children in a new environment when someone else says it is time creates stress for both them and their preschoolers. Trust your instincts and your own inner guidance when it comes to separations, especially those involving well-meaning early childhood experts.

Watch your young child for signs that he is overwhelmed with the amount of separation you're giving him. Respect your child when she says she isn't ready for you to leave yet. Never let someone talk you into just leaving because your child will "be fine in a minute." Children's words and behaviors will tell you when they are ready for separation. Sometimes you may need to evaluate the situation and perhaps delay separation until your child is older and more ready to handle those challenges. Having to deal with separation before they are ready puts children into survival mode, the red-light state. Just forcing a child to handle the separation will not benefit the child in the long term. When they are ready, just like when they start to walk or talk, separation just happens naturally—no pushing necessary.

If separation is absolutely necessary before a child is really ready for it, consider seeking support using integrative story sharing. Many times, a child not quite ready for separation has an earlier stuck point. I worked with one six-year-old who wasn't ready to separate from her parents; she had always been slow to move through transitions and would do so only when it was her idea. She was able to transition peacefully into school after we created the space for her to share her birth story and show her experience of it.

Allow "babyish" behaviors and meet the expressed need. Parents often say that the child needs to stop a behavior because he or she is "too old" for it. Most parenting information focuses on labeling behaviors as good or bad, appropriate or inappropriate, and making the bad, inappropriate ones go away. But the guiding principles tell us something different. Principle 1 says that all behavior is communication, and principle 3 reminds us that unmet needs do not just go away.

Behaviors that look babyish are a communication of an unmet need. Find the unmet need and meet it, and the behavior will go away when the child is ready. Sometimes it means that a child needs to integrate an experience from early in his life, such as his traumatic birth, or a prolonged separation when he was very young. There are many ways to repair those early relationship breaks and reconnect in this present moment. Meeting this need is much easier to do now than when your child gets bigger. Unmet needs have a tendency to grow with the child, growing into behaviors that are bigger, too. We might be able to get our child to stop a behavior we deem undesirable or age-inappropriate, but unless we recognize and meet the need that behavior is communicating, another one will just pop up in its place. For example, parents might put yucky tasting stuff on their child's thumb to get her to stop sucking it. After a few weeks with more than the usual number of meltdowns, the child finally stops. Parents declare victory. Then they notice their child is now twirling her hair into knots and rocking back and forth.

In the thumb-sucking example, what might parents do instead of putting something on the child's thumb or just telling her not to suck it? First, realize that this behavior is communicating a need: a child who sucks her thumb is most likely doing so when she is stressed out. So you'll need to help her develop more coping skills and learn to reach out to others when she is feeling overwhelmed.

When you see her with her thumb in her mouth, pull her onto your lap without saying anything about the thumb-sucking. Later, when the stressor is behind her, tell her that you noticed she sucks her thumb when she's feeling stress—or having "big feelings," or whatever words work best. Then ask her to come to you when she feels like sucking her thumb, and when she does, invite her to sit on your lap. Inviting her to come and sit on your lap creates a positive association between stress and human contact, and that association respects the underlying communication of the behavior.

Even more important than waiting until it happens is to create the space to be proactive. How long has your child been sucking her thumb? What was going on when it started? Is there a story your child needs to hear that can help make sense of why she once needed to suck her thumb? By being curious about the feelings that surround thumb-sucking—both your daughter's feelings and your own—you just might make a connection and understand what she really needs and where that need came from.

Continue lots of close physical contact and "time in." Our children need lots of continued physical contact long after infancy. Children with a strong attachment will seek out physical touch and comfort when they are feeling overwhelmed. Pick them up and carry them when they ask to be carried. Spend time with your child rocking in a rocking chair at the end of the day. Go swimming with your child and play little games in the water together. Take baths together. Lay down with your children and hold them at night when it is time to sleep, or be in close physical proximity if they won't allow you to hold them.

When behavior issues arise, practice time in, rather than time out. Our children need to connect with us and, by doing so, learn to regulate themselves, rather than be isolated for misbehavior. Teaching moments are not in our red-light moments when the negative behavior is happening, but rather afterward, when no one is in survival mode. This teaching time might be five minutes or five hours after the behavior. It doesn't mean that everyone needs to be perfectly calm, but rather that everyone is in a place where they can connect with the feelings of the others. The moment after something happens is a time to reconnect. A behavior issue signals a disconnection in the relationship, or within oneself, and is an opportunity for you and your child to reconnect.

Chances are that our children aren't going to learn from us if all we do is give them a list of reasons why it isn't OK to do whatever they just did; they're going to learn through hearing us tell stories and by practicing the appropriate behaviors through games and acting out the stories.

Teach your child appropriate behaviors through modeling. If you aren't doing it, don't expect your child to do it, either. Modeling the behaviors you want your young children to imitate is one of the most important things you can do for them. They are little recorders and will learn by example, rather than any words you may say to them. If you don't want them to yell, model talking softly and respectfully. Many times the very behaviors that annoy us are ones that we are modeling for them. The word *discipline* means "to teach," so teach your children what you want them to do by showing them what to do. When you make a mistake, repair it. Tell them you are sorry that you spoke to them in a harsh tone and that they don't deserve to have anyone talk to them like that. And then revisit the situation, this time doing what you wish you'd done the first time. In doing so, you are showing your children that everyone makes mistakes, and you are modeling how to correct those mistakes.

Strive to be emotionally present with your child and spend time connecting with her every day. Invest in time connecting with your children. Connect before you go off to work and school, connect before breakfast, connect in the middle of the day, connect before bed, and connect when coming back together after a separation. *Connection Parenting* author Pam Leo says, "The level of cooperation you receive from your child is equal to the level of connection in the relationship." When you prioritize the relationship and time with your child, your child feels important and is more likely to cooperate. Many parents share how simply making an effort to connect more often with their children results in big shifts in overall cooperation and peace in the family.

There is a big difference between just spending time in our child's physical presence and connecting with them while being 100 percent emotionally present. Many parents practicing attachment parenting, for example, say that they are with their children 24/7, yet when they start to look at how much quality connected time they actually spend with their children, they're surprised by how little it actually is.

Emotional connection means that you are focused only on your child—what they are saying and doing. It means that you are letting go of the long list of things you need to be doing or should be doing instead of sitting with your child while he plays with blocks. It means letting the phone go unanswered, not responding to that text message, and turning off the television. What a strong message our children get when our actions tell them a phone call, email, or text message is less important to us than being with them right now, doing what *they* want to do.

Some parents start by asking themselves to pay 100 percent attention to their child for one minute and find even this proves to be a challenge for them. We simply aren't used to paying focused attention to others in this world of multitasking. Our children need us to be single-taskers during our time with them, and the most important single task we have every day is to spend this time connecting with our children.

Connect before you ask your children to do anything. So many times, we, in our adult minds, simply see all that must be done, and we miss the opportunity to connect with our children. Children who are connected to a parent are much more likely to be cooperative and are generally much more pleasant to be around. When we spend a few minutes learning about what they just built with their blocks, they will be much more likely to say yes when we then ask if they would be willing to put the blocks away. When our children say no to such a request, we can seek more understanding by asking questions: Why did you say no? Do you want to keep what you built? Do you want Daddy to see it first? What if we took a picture of the building before we put the blocks away? This line of questions can make a big difference in creating connection with our children. It says loud and clear, "I care about what matters to you. Together, we can find a way to make this work."

"Connect before you correct," says Pam Leo. Before you tell your children they just did something wrong, take a few minutes to connect with them. Ask how they're feeling or state an observation about what you are seeing on their face, for example. Get down on their level and pull them in close, if they'll let you. Spend a few minutes just being with your children. And make sure that you are both able to connect before you try to talk about a specific behavior.

Your intention is just as important, if not more important, than any action you take or words you may use. When your child has just hit another child, for example, it is easy to launch into an explanation of why it is wrong to hit other children and what your child is supposed to do instead. However, if we first stop and meet our child where he is—in his frustration, disappointment, or fear—we can go a long way toward actually helping our child to change the behavior, because we demonstrate that someone understands him and is trying to help.

Brain Development 101:
Three- to Five-Year-Olds

Between three and five years old, children are *emotional brain dominant.*

Behaviors: Their behaviors are primarily imitative with a twist of intelligence that makes you think they're smarter and more logical than they really are at this age.

Stress response: Children of this age tend to be quite vocal about how they feel when things don't go their way. Their emotional brain is coming more online now, and we will know exactly how our children feel about everything—good or bad. Children of this age no longer have only the fight, flight, or freeze response; some children have a well-worn set of neural pathways that leads them to have striking reactions

(continued)

---

when stressed. Well-regulated children of this age can calm their own stress, but still *need the support of emotionally healthy adults, who don't take their behaviors personally,* to calm down or co-regulate. Not taking their behaviors personally can be a real challenge during this stage of parenting.

Regulatory ability: Those children who have had their early attachment needs met and haven't experienced overwhelming trauma will generally be able to regulate their own stress response (calm themselves down). They still need to be pulled in close when they are overwhelmed and need someone to guide them away from overwhelming situations. The regulatory ability of those who haven't had their early needs met will look much more like what was described in "Brain Development 101: Infants" earlier in this chapter. They may rapidly shift back and forth from their chronological age to a much younger emotional age when overwhelmed.

Means of learning: Children this age learn primarily through observation of what parents are modeling for them. They will unconsciously imitate everything you do (for better or for worse).

Memory: The part of the brain responsible for storing and archiving memories is developing, and children this age may start to retain conscious memories. Everything goes into the templates created during the first three years.

(continued)

Strategies for creating relationships with three- to five-year-olds, based on brain development: Touch, continued breastfeeding and co-sleeping (as long as it is mutually agreeable), or similar efforts to hold, rock, and be close to our children. Give children opportunities to join you in your adult tasks (such as letting them help you make dinner and do what you are doing). Respect your children's need to express feelings, while still setting appropriate limits. Engage in the strategies appropriate for younger children if they are acting emotionally much younger than their chronological age.

Avoid: Time out. Your children still need your physical and emotional presence when they are upset and emotional, but they also need you to set healthy limits. For more suggestions on setting limits, see the next chapter's section on handling tantrums.

Questions to Ponder

- How do you feel about breastfeeding? What about extended breastfeeding? How does your partner feel about these things? Were you breastfed? Was your partner breastfed?

- Where did you sleep growing up? What do you know about your sleep patterns as a child? What are they like as an adult? Do you see any relationship between the two? Where do you believe young children should sleep?

- If something isn't working for your family, be willing to look deeper. Did the current pattern begin with something that happened earlier in your child's life? Seek support if you are struggling with your child's behavior in any area, including transitioning a child to sleeping on her own or transitioning him away from breastfeeding when you're no longer able to stay connected while you're doing it.

- How are you meeting your own needs as a parent as your child grows older? What is your biggest challenge?

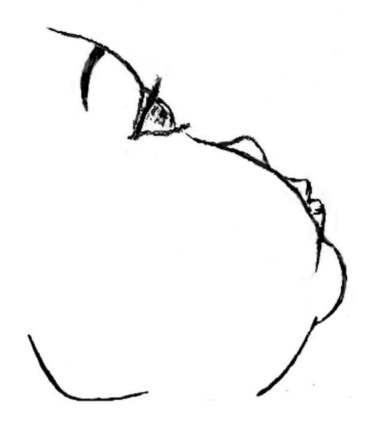

Chapter Four

Challenges to Creating Connection:
Tantrums, Car Seats, Single Parenthood,
Working Parents and Special Situations

Tantrums

I think the questions I'm most frequently asked are about emotional outbursts. Whether their child is two or twelve, parents have a difficult time knowing how to handle tantrums with love and respect.

Most parenting information says to ignore the behavior, while other information suggests that our child needs to be punished or removed from our presence when they are having a tantrum so as to not "reward the negative behavior." But remember what the first of consciously parenting's guiding principles says: all behavior is communication. What underlying needs are your children trying to express through their tantrums?

Sometimes our children are expressing frustration from the stresses of their day and just need someone to hear how difficult it has been for them. It is hard work being two or three or four or thirty-five. Everyone needs someone to hear them and validate them, to let them know someone cares that their day has been so difficult.

Children have very real stressors that we, as a society, tend to minimize. One mother I knew was perplexed by her daughter's daily temper tantrums, which seemed to be happening when she was leaving for work and returning from work. Shirley's two year-old daughter, Kelly, was being cared for during the day by her grandmother. Kelly loved her grandma and looked forward to being with her, but she was also sad that she had to separate from her mother. At the end of the day, she was sad because her grandma was going home. Shirley took all of this sadness personally. She was feeling some guilt about needing to go to work, so her daughter's expressions were painful for her. She had tried everything to make those tantrums stop, but they seemed to be getting worse.

Kelly was experiencing a very real stressor in her life, and she needed someone to hear how difficult it was that she had to make those transitions—from Mom's care to Grandma's care, then back to Mom's care—and make them at times when she was tired, hungry, or both. I suggested that Shirley spend some time with her own feelings about the situation, including the fact that she was working when she would rather be home with her daughter. She decided to write about her feelings and share what she wrote with a friend, allowing herself to feel her own feelings in a safe place. Doing so gave her more emotional space to handle her daughter's feelings.

The next day, Kelly had her predictable tantrum when her grandma was leaving. This time, Shirley sat down on the floor near her daughter and, while giving her some space, said, "I know it is hard when Grandma leaves. It is hard when someone we love leaves." The words themselves weren't as important as the feeling Shirley felt as she said them. Before she spoke, she connected with her own experiences of people she loved leaving her, so she was really feeling the truth of what she said. She later told me:

> Her crying got louder when I started saying the words about how hard it must be for her to have Grandma leave. I was a little worried at first, but then the quality of the crying changed. Normally her tantrums have a whiny quality to them, but this time the whiny shifted into a very sad cry. She cried by herself with me nearby for about five minutes before she crawled into my lap and cried some more. After another five minutes, she stopped crying and began to calm down. I continued to hold her on my lap. It was incredible. Most of her tantrums in the past were lasting up to an hour. This small shift in how I was handling it shortened it down to ten minutes! I nearly jumped back in the car to e-mail you and tell you what had happened. It was a miracle.

Kelly's tantrums continued to get shorter over the course of several days until there were no more tantrums. Shirley was able to observe where her daughter was and how she was feeling, so that she could connect with her daughter's feelings and give her daughter words for her experience. Today, there are still some days when Kelly falls apart as Mom walks through the door, but she is relatively calm most days now that her underlying need is addressed. Her behavior was a communication, and Shirley was finally able to hear what she was saying. When a child feels heard, the tantrums often stop, as they no longer serve a purpose.

If we try to use a consequence to take care of an unmet need, we will not succeed.

Pam Leo, in her book *Connection Parenting*, talks about how tantrums are caused by either a full "hurts cup," where there is simply no more space for pain and it spills out, or an empty "love cup," where there is a lack of connection with the people most important to the child (parents or other primary caregivers). When we can address the unmet needs and our children's feelings, really hearing what our children are saying through their tantrums, they can get through the feelings and past the need to have a tantrum.

Car Seats

Car seats are a necessary evil in the lives of parents. In most states, car seats are mandatory for all children under the age of four, though California recently passed a law that all children under age eight must be restrained in a car seat. Inside a car, children are safest when they are safely and properly secured in a car seat. But for many children, being in the car seat is a separation from their parents that they would rather not experience. Even older children at times are less than excited about being contained somewhere outside of your loving arms. The car seat provides us with a perfect situation for exploring how we can set limits while still being responsive to and respectful of our children.

Before you put your baby in the car seat to go somewhere, spend time holding and feeding her. Always plan extra time so that you are not rushed. If your baby fusses, attend to her. You cannot always make your baby happy in the car seat, but you can always acknowledge that your baby is having feelings about being in the car. If it is not possible to stop the car, put a hand back for your baby to hold, place your hand on his head, and sing or talk to him. Not responding to baby in the car doesn't teach him that he needs to be quiet in the car. It teaches him that no one cares about him.

When our children get older, it is common for us to have difficulty getting them happily into the car seat. As they get older and larger, becoming toddlers with their own ideas and opinions about such things, it can be more of a challenge to physically place them into a car seat unless we have another person to help us. Although it is true that we are bigger and stronger than our child, I cannot recommend forcing a child to do something just because we are bigger and stronger. Instead, we need to get a little more creative and embrace this wonderful opportunity to set a limit and talk about what that limit really means for our toddler.

We might institute a rule saying that everyone needs to be buckled in when the car is moving, so that everyone is safe. With very young children, making getting into the car a game or something fun can really help with the transition from our arms to the car seat. If they start to fuss while going into the car seat, let them know that you see that they are upset, and connect with their feelings about it: "Mama's sad that you're out of my arms, too." Having special toys that are only for car rides can be an effective way to help with the transition. If a child is upset, climb into the car and help her calm down before attempting to buckle her into the car seat. Or buckle him in and then sit next to him for a few minutes until he calms down. It is better to remove an upset child from a car seat and spend a few minutes connecting with him than to just climb into the driver's seat and go. Remember that there is nothing more important than your relationship—nothing.

We can be responsive to our child's feelings even if we need to set a limit.

Sometimes a child gets very upset every time parents place her in a car seat. This was certainly true for Sofia, whose parents came to me when she was three months old. Since she was born, she had been crying every time she was placed in the car seat. As we began exploring what had happened on her very early car trips, Denny, Sofia's father, explained how the first car trip after her birth was to the hospital. Sofia had a fever at one day old, and the pediatrician told them to go to the hospital for treatment. But Heather, Sofia's mom, was unable to travel after a very difficult birth.

I helped Denny and Heather use integrative story sharing to tell Sofia the story of this trip, when Sofia had to be separated from her mother. Baby Sofia cried as Denny and Heather shared the story with her, getting very loud when Denny told the part about driving away without Mommy. Heather expressed her feelings, telling Sofia how sad she was to not have her in her arms right after she was born and that being apart just felt wrong.

After they finished telling the story, they listened to Sofia share her version of the story, through her expressions and her feelings. I then suggested that every time they were going to get into the car, they talk to Sofia about what was going to happen. Every time they got into the car, they would retell the story of what happened on Sofia's first car ride. Then they would tell her that for this car ride, they were going to Starbucks or Home Depot or to Grandma's house *together* and that they would all be coming back together. Every time she cried in the car, they talked to her about what had happened in the past and what was happening now.

Later, they told me how one time, Denny was taking Sofia out in the car while Heather was resting. Sofia started crying as soon as she was buckled into the seat. Denny talked to her about what was happening, and she almost immediately stopped crying. Her dad had heard her and understood, so she didn't need to cry any more. (For more on integrative story sharing, see the audio program "Little People, Big Challenges: Car Seats" at www.consciouslyparenting.com/LPBC.)

Our children often have their own story about whatever is happening to them in the car seat. Seek to understand the communication and what it must be like from your child's perspective. If you find yourself thinking about a previous experience as you listen to your child cry, pay attention to that, as it may help you figure out what is going on for him and how you can help. When the underlying need is met, it will go away.

Single Parenthood

Sometimes, either through choice, such as when a single parent adopts a child, or through life circumstances, such as death or divorce, we may find ourselves parenting our children alone. When we are creating a relationship with our children, the most labor-intensive time of our parenting experience, we need as much support as possible. No one person can be everything to everyone, and this is especially true for single parents. In order to truly meet both our children's needs and our own, we need to make sure that we create a community of support for ourselves and for our families, as guiding principle 8 of consciously parenting reminds us. Such community support is even more necessary when we are parenting a child with a trauma as part of her story.

One grandmother raising her grandchildren commented that there was never any time for her to take care of herself. Iwould argue that there isn't time for her to *not* take care of herself. If we don't find a way to meet our own needs, we cannot possibly take care of our children's needs. For that reason, it is essential that we find others who can support us.

When they really start to explore the idea of asking for help, many parents hit a brick wall. They don't know who to ask or what to ask for. They feel guilty that they are unable to do everything themselves. After all, they had or adopted this child, so feel like they should be able to care for her. However, once parents start thinking about it, many start to come up with names of people who might want to come and play with their child once a week (and, in fact, may be delighted to have the opportunity) or who would be willing to bring in a meal. Others think of friends who enjoy cleaning and might be willing to offer some help. Some families find other like-minded parents at church, while others look to play groups or other community organizations. (For more information on creating community, please see Chapter 9: Connecting in Community, Connecting to Ourselves of Book I: *Consciously Parenting: What it Really Takes to Raise Emotionally Healthy Families*.) Don't overlook those folks who no longer have children at home. These are often the people with the time and attention available to give to some-one else, as well as an understanding of what it is like to have young children around. No matter where you find your commu-nity, the most important thing is to realize that others are often happy to help you. Most of the time, we just haven't asked.

If you are a single parent, find ways to simplify life as much as possible. Eliminate nonessential tasks. If possible, pay someone to do the things you don't have time to get to right now. (See the following section, "Working Parents," and Isabelle Fox's ideas to pay for essentials so we can be present with our children when they're little.) There will always be laundry and dishes to wash, but your child is young for just a short time.

Remember, the most important thing is your relation-ship with your child. Find ways to prioritize the relationship, and things will go much more smoothly for everyone. If you have a choice between washing the dishes or listening to what your child did at school that day, choose listening to your child. If, after the children are in bed, what you really want to do is relax in the bathtub rather than clean it, choose to take care of your own need for relaxation and have that bath. Most importantly, don't let others decide what tasks are essential or what should be the priority. Your mother may make disparaging comments about the unvacuumed rug, but is satisfying her standards of cleanliness more important than spending time with your children? Let your inner guidance decide what's important and what isn't, which tasks support the relationship with your child and which don't.

When faced with a particular task, ask yourself whether doing it will help your children learn to regulate their emotions, contribute to the relationship you're creating with your children, or meet a need of your own. Sometimes the answer is yes: "I need to do the dishes so that we can make breakfast in the morning." In these cases, still take the time to connect with your child first. After you've connected, your children may be willing and able to join you in your tasks.

Working Parents

Babies *need* our physical and emotional presence. Even though babies can't remember consciously, they do know when we are there with them or not, and babies are indeed affected when they are separated from their primary caregiver for long stretches of time. If you must work, consider alternative schedules, taking your baby to work with you (perhaps with another caregiver who can be primarily in charge of your baby, but will bring the baby to you when he or she needs you), or arranging to work from home as much as possible.

Isabelle Fox, author of *Being There: The Benefits of a Stay-at-Home Parent,* suggests that parents consider taking out a loan so that someone can stay home with a new baby for the first two years of his or her life. We think nothing of getting a mortgage or taking out a loan on a car, but it doesn't cross our minds to take out a loan to stay home with our children, the most valuable of our "possessions". By the time our children are around the age of two, they are more able to understand that Mom or Dad is going to work and will be back again, and they are also verbal enough to tell us if something doesn't feel good when they are being cared for by someone else. There is nothing more important than consistent, loving care for our young children—nothing.

If you must be separated from your baby, find a loving environment, preferably with a relative, where your baby can be cared for. People who are related to a baby will generally give better care than a nonrelative. When eight-month-old Evan's mom returned to her job as a flight attendant, his father and grandmother cared for him. The best situation is for children to have one substitute caregiver or perhaps two relatives, ideally parents or grandparents, consistently in their lives in addition to their primary caregiver. Having someone come to your home to look after your baby is ideal. The fewer changes your baby experiences, the better. Family daycare centers can also be good options. Use your instincts and ask yourself, "Would *I* want to spend my day with this person in this environment?" If you wouldn't, why would your baby?

When you and your baby are together, spend as much time as possible in close physical contact, skin-to-skin. Practice safe co-sleeping. (If their moms are gone all day, some babies will reverse-cycle nurse, doing most of their feeding at night.) Spend as much time together as possible connecting with each other. There is no better investment you can make as a parent. Talk to your baby about how hard it feels to be away from each other during the day. Share your own feelings of sadness and regret. Allow your baby to cry and express her feelings about it, too. You may not be able to change the situation, but you can always listen to your baby's feelings about it. If it is too painful for you to do so, seek the support of someone who can listen to your feelings about the situation. When you make room for your own feelings and allow them, you'll have room for your baby's feelings and experience, too.

Simplify your life and eliminate nonessential tasks. Your baby needs you to be emotionally present as much as possible when you are together. Continue breastfeeding whenever possible to continue building the bond of your relationship.

Creating Connection Following Trauma: A Case Study

Faith had become a parent very early in life and parented the only way she knew how—the same way that she was raised. Thankfully, her parents had been fairly attuned to her needs, and she found parenting to be rather instinctive for her. She was able to easily meet the needs of her son. Her son was an easy baby to soothe and a joy to spend time with. Life circumstances found her a single mother when her son was two, and she had to work full time, putting him in daycare. She worked hard to keep food on the table for him and to meet his basic needs.

Faith later got remarried, and she and her second husband, Darrell, very much wanted to have children. During Faith's second pregnancy, Darrell lost his job, so there was a great deal of stress during that time for the whole family. Christopher's birth was complicated, and Faith nearly died from a hemorrhage following an emergency C-section. Both Faith and Darrell were somewhat in shock after the dramatic turn of events surrounding Christopher's birth, and neither really knew how to begin to create a relationship with him. Christopher was a totally different baby than her first son had been: he was "high need" and difficult to soothe, and there was not quite as much joy involved in caring for him. Faith and Darrell did the best they could, but things seemed to only get further out of control. Sleep was a nightmare from the beginning and only got worse as Christopher grew older. At age three, he was still fighting sleep every night, usually until 11 p.m. He had multiple temper tantrums every day. When his tired parents came to see me, they were at their wits' end. How could they start creating a positive relationship?

What Christopher needed was to release the energy stored from the trauma of his birth. Both of his parents had been too overwhelmed to really be present and meet his early emotional needs at that time. We started with some very simple exercises to facilitate Christopher's bonding and connection with both parents and soothe his stress. For example, the parents took turns giving Christopher a massage on alternate days; both parents spent time each day holding him and rocking him, and bottle-feeding Christopher a sweet milk. I also suggested that Faith and Darrel find and work with a somatically oriented play therapist to help Christopher process and integrate the traumatic birth experience. More on Christopher's healing journey can be found in the fourth book of the Consciously Parenting series on repairing relationships: *Healing Connection.*

Creating Connection after Adoption: A Case Study

Sage and Ronald had wanted to have children, but Sage had a medical issue that prevented her from sustaining a pregnancy. After looking at all of their options, they decided to adopt a child from Ukraine. While they were waiting for the green light, Sage began to research the special issues and needs of an adopted child. She came upon attachment research and read everything she could find regarding attachment with an older child. She learned that early needs that weren't met don't go away and that she and Ronald would need to focus their attention on meeting those early developmental needs. One of her favorite books was *Beyond Consequences, Logic, and Control,* written by Bryan Post and Heather T. Forbes, and she read it repeatedly while waiting to travel to Ukraine to bring their child home. In this book, she learned about the special needs of adopted children and how they are often in a perpetual state of survival (a red-light state). They may be shut down (hypoaroused), or they may be agitated and aggressive (hyperaroused).

When Sage and Ronald were finally able to bring six-year-old Robert home, Sage knew she had to parent him as if he were a much younger child. Robert had spent most of his first six years in an orphanage with a ratio of one adult to every ten infants, so his early needs for love, affection, care, and protection had not been met. She knew that emotionally he was probably much closer to two years old than six years old. She struggled to understand exactly what it would be like to parent a much younger child, since she and Ronald had never had other children. She continued to read everything she could.

When they brought Robert home, they decided to make his world very small. They kept visits with other family members to a minimum and did not enroll him in school right away. They knew that meeting his early developmental needs was far more important for him than going off to school. The lessons he needed most were about love, not arithmetic. They followed his cues and respected his wishes for space or for closeness. After just a short time, Robert was able to tolerate his father holding him and giving him short massages at night. They added rocking and bottle-feeding with sweet milk, experiences designed to meet his unmet developmental needs, and they created a daily routine that was suitable for a much younger child. They responded lovingly to his expressed cues as if he were only two years old. In about a year's time, Robert was ready to handle being separated from his new parents, and the stressors of school. Though he struggled with his English and needed special accommodations at school, addressing his early unmet needs made his transition into his new family practically seamless.

Questions to Ponder

- What are your biggest challenges and/or special situations as a parent?

- What are your partner's biggest challenges and/or special situations as a parent?

- How can you begin to shift your understanding of what is happening with your child? What is the underlying need? What is your child attempting to communicate to you through her behaviors?

Conclusion

Everyone's personal story begins with the moment of their conception and includes all their experiences in the womb, during birth, and in their early years. Even though we cannot remember them consciously, our early experiences leave an indelible print on our hearts and minds. Most of us have never considered how our own early story may be impacting us now, in our personal life and in our relationships with our own children.

As expectant and new parents, it is helpful to understand that events from our own early lives, as well as events in our child's early life, can have a profound effect on the connection between us. When we understand that the beginning matters, we have more information to use when making decisions, and a new perspective to help us repair the relationship if we're stuck. If we are parenting older children, understanding the impact of the beginning of our relationship can help us to better understand the relationship's long-standing patterns and start to shift them.

Our babies and young children need attentive, conscious parenting to help them through their emotional upsets, so they can learn to co-regulate, or regulate their emotions in connection with another person. Responsive parenting can mean following attachment parenting ideas, including breastfeeding, babywearing, keeping the baby close to you at night, and responding to nighttime needs. Responsive parenting includes noticing what is working or not working for you, and recognizing that how you feel when you are doing something is just as important as what you're doing. If something isn't working for you, be curious about why it isn't and get support if you need it.

As our children grow and stretch their wings a bit, they need us to continue to be responsive to their needs. We can support our children through transitions, especially when they seem to revert to younger behaviors. This is a sign that we need to slow down and connect more, not less.

Conclusion

Regardless of how the relationship with our child began or has been going, we have the power to make a shift and to create connection in our relationship with each and every moment we have together.

Appendix 1

Contrasting Behavior-Focused and Relationship-Centered Parenting

The following table contrasts the consciously parenting paradigm with that of traditional parenting. When we are using traditional parenting behaviors and techniques, our children are going to survive. But consciously parenting allows our children to *thrive!*

Since most of us were parented according to traditional parenting information, we will find that sometimes behavior-focused strategies sneak into our parenting. When that happens, we should not judge ourselves. Instead, we can remember to simply use our newfound awareness to make different choices.

Note: The following chart is meant to create awareness of parenting choices that tend to emphasize a focus on the behavior versus a focus on the relationship. However, just because someone bottle-feeds doesn't mean that they are not consciously parenting. This chart is only meant to create awareness and for you to ask questions about why you are making the choices you are making, rather than as a judgment about what is right or wrong. Even parents who are consciously parenting fall into patterns of more traditional parenting. And a stroller can be a useful tool if it isn't a primary parenting strategy.

Traditional Parenting (Behavior Focused)	Consciously Parenting (Relationship Centered)
Physical distance (strollers, car seats, cribs)	Physical closeness (slings, rocking, holding)
Bottle-feeding	Breastfeeding
Sleep training, Solitary sleeping	Co-sleeping, shared sleeping
Focus on behaviors	Focus on relationship
Focus on needs of parents only	Focus on needs of the baby, while respecting parents' needs and feelings as the baby grows
Punishment and consequences	Understanding dysregulation and the communication of behaviors
Time out	Time in

Appendix 2

The Guiding Principles of Consciously Parenting

Principle 1: All behavior is a communication. Behavior reflects the internal state of the individual and the relationship's level of connection.

Principle 2: The parent-child relationship is more important than any behavioral intervention, consequence, or punishment.

Principle 3: Children unfold neurosequentially, and quality, connected relationships allow for the unfolding. A need met will go away; a need unmet is here to stay.

Principle 4: Behaviors occur on a continuum. Behaviors in children (and parents, too) correlate to the parents' own neurodevelopment and attachment status.

Principle 5: Parental interpretation of behaviors comes from both a conscious and subconscious place, resulting in positive or negative neurophysiologic feedback loops.

Principle 6: All individuals have a right and a responsibility to learn to express their feelings appropriately. Feelings allow us to connect to our internal guidance system.

Principle 7: Children need boundaries. We can set appropriate limits for our children while still respecting their needs and feelings—if we are aware of ourselves. (We can ask, for example, "Is this about me? Is this about them? Are my children communicating a need? Is the boundary I'm setting necessary, or is this situation an opportunity for me to grow?")

Principle 8: No man is an island. We need to create communities of support for ourselves and for our children. We need to take care of ourselves so that we can take care of our children.

Resources

Books

Affect Dysregulation and Disorders of the Self by Allan N. Schore

Attached at the Heart: 8 Proven Parenting Principles for Raising Connected and Compassionate Children by Barbara Nicholson and Lysa Parker

Becoming Attached: First Relationships and How They Shape Our Capacity to Love by Robert Karen

Biology of Belief by Bruce Lipton

The Boy Who Was Raised as a Dog by Bruce Perry

Connection Parenting: Parenting through Connection instead of Coercion, Through Love instead of Fear by Pam Leo, website: www.connectionparenting.com

The Continuum Concept by Jean Liedloff

The Family Bed by Tine Thevenin

Healing Trauma: Attachment, Mind, Body, and Brain, Edited by Marion F. Solomon and Daniel J. Siegel

The Healing Power of Emotion: Affective Neuroscience, Development, and Clinical Practice, Edited by Diana Fosha, Daniel J. Siegel, and Marion F. Solomon

Hold Me Tight: Seven Conversations for a Lifetime of Love by Dr. Sue Johnson, website: www.iceeft.com

<u>Immaculate Deception II: Myth, Magic, and Birth</u> by Suzanne Arms, website: www.birthingthefuture.org

<u>Keeping the Love You Find: A Personal Guide</u> by Harville Hendrix

<u>Let the Baby Drive: Navigating the Road of New Motherhood</u> by Lu Hanessian, websites: www.letthebabydrive.com, and www.parent2parentu.com

<u>The Making and Breaking of Affectional Bonds</u> by John Bowlby

<u>Molecules of Emotion: Why You Feel the Way You Feel</u> by Candace B. Pert, PhD

<u>The Neurobiology of "We": How Relationships, the Mind, and the Brain Interact to Shape Who We Are</u> by Daniel Seigel (audio book)

<u>Opening Up: The Healing Power of Expressing Emotions</u> by James Pennebaker

<u>Parenting From the Inside Out: How a Deeper Self-Understanding Can Help You Raise Children Who Thrive</u> by Daniel J. Siegel and Mary Hartzell

<u>Playing in the Unified Field: Raising and Becoming Conscious, Creative Human Beings</u> by Carla Hannaford

<u>Raising Our Children, Raising Ourselves: Transforming parent-child relationships from reaction and struggle to freedom, power and joy</u> by Naomi Aldort

<u>Real Love</u> by Greg Baer

The Science of Parenting: How today's brain research can help you raise happy, emotionally balanced children by Margot Sunderland

Three in a Bed: The Benefits of Sleeping With Your Baby by Deborah Jackson

Trauma Through a Child's Eyes: Awakening the Ordinary Miracle of Healing by Peter A Levine and Maggie Kline

Waking the Tiger: Healing Trauma by Peter Levine

Why Love Matters: How Affection Shapes a Baby's Brain by Sue Gerhardt

The Womanly Art of Breastfeeding published by La Leche League, website: www.llli.org

Writing Down Your Soul: How to Activate and Listen to the Extraordinary Voice Within by Janet Conner, website www.janetconner.com

You Can Heal Your Life by Louise Hay

Additional Resources

Attachment Parenting International, website
www.attachmentparenting.org

Babywearing International, website
www.babywearinginternational.org

Birthing the Future, website www.birthingthefuture.org

Carrie Contey, website www.slowfamilyliving.com

Cloth Diapering 101 from Mothering:
http://bit.ly/clothdiapering101

Cloth Diapering 101 Digital Reprint from Mothering:
www.motheringshop.com/product-p/digreprint-cloth.htm

Connection Parenting, website: www.connectionparenting.com

Hedy Schleifer, LMHC, website: www.hedyyumi.com

Holistic Moms Network, website www.holisticmoms.org

Infant Massage USA, website www.infantmassageusa.org

International Chiropractic Pediatric Association, website:
www.icpa4kids.com

Interview with Janet Conner:
www.consciouslyparenting.com/teleseminars/JanetConner1.php

Kindred Community, website www.kindredcommunity.com

La Leche League International, website www.llli.org

Mothering Magazine, website www.mothering.com

Parent2ParentU, website www.parent2parentu.com

Parenting Beyond Behaviors DVD Set by Rebecca Thompson:
www.consciouslyparenting.com/store/pbb.php

Pathways to Family Wellness Magazine, website
www.pathwaystofamilywellness.org

Ray Castellino and Mary Jackson, *Little People, Big Challenges.*
www.consciouslyparenting.com/LPBC
Website: www.aboutconnections.com

William Sears, MD. Website: www.askdrsears.com

Reactive Attachment Disorder Resources:

Dr. Daniel Amen, Amen Clinics: http://www.amenclinics.net

Eric Guy, Center for Victory: www.centerforvictory.com

Dr. Bruce Perry, <u>The Boy Who Was Raised as a Dog</u>,
www.childtrauma.org

Karyn Purvis: http://empoweredtoconnect.org